If I Ever Get Out Of
This World Alive

Also by the author:

I Wasn't Made For These Times – 2004
I'm Not Like Everybody Else – 2017

If I Ever Get Out Of This World Alive

A collection of short stories and poetry
exploring themes of rock and roll and death
during the Covid-19 pandemic

Richard Dalgety

Matador
9 Priory Business Park,
Wistow Road, Kibworth Beauchamp,
Leicestershire. LE8 0RX
Tel: 0116 279 2299
Email: books@troubador.co.uk
Web: www.troubador.co.uk/matador
Twitter: @matadorbooks

ISBN 978 1800462 588
British Library Cataloguing in Publication Data.
A catalogue record for this book is available from the British Library.

Printed and bound in the UK by TJ Books Limited, Padstow, Cornwall
Typeset in 11pt Minion Pro by Troubador Publishing Ltd, Leicester, UK

Matador is an imprint of Troubador Publishing Ltd

It is my ambition to say in ten sentences what others say in a whole book

Friedrich Nietzsche

Can I see another's woe, and not be in sorrow too? Can I see another's grief and not seek for kind relief?

William Blake

CONTENTS

Poems

AUTHOR'S FOREWORD

I have always been fascinated by the history of rock-and-roll music. I can spend entire weekends devouring books, magazines, films and documentaries on the subject. The most exciting moments in my life are intertwined with rock-and-roll history – seeing Jeff Buckley at Glastonbury Festival in 1995 just after finishing my A Levels. Going to the Libertines gig at the Kentish Town Forum in 2003 just after Pete Doherty had been released from prison for raiding his bandmate Carl Barat's flat. Immersing myself in Dublin in 2016 during and after Bruce Springsteen's momentous set at Croke Park, when it felt like the entire city became a rock-and-roll concert for twenty-four hours.

Like the lead character in Nick Hornby's *High Fidelity*, I define myself by my top fives – top five albums (*Led Zeppelin II, Astral Weeks, London Calling, Nebraska, Marquee Moon*), top five films (*Trainspotting, Withnail and I, Butch Cassidy and the Sundance Kid, Back to the Future, The Shawshank Redemption*), top five books (*A Tale of Two Cities, Brighton Rock, The Buddha of Suburbia, On the Road, Zen and the Art of Motorcycle Maintenance*), top five ex-girlfriends. If you really wanted to f**k me up you should have got to me earlier!

It is the rock-and-roll top fives that I spend the most time thinking about. Who were the top five rock-and-roll artists of the fifties? Buddy Holly, Elvis Presley, Chuck Berry, Eddie Cochran and Little Richard. But then can you throw Johnny Cash in there? Was he rock and roll? What about Jerry Lee Lewis or Gene Vincent?

I started putting this book together in March 2020, when another huge topic dominated my mind – death. I thought a lot about my own death and then realised that the Covid-19 outbreak meant that death was all around me, an unpredicted global pandemic affecting every country on the planet. Everyone's work and social lives were hugely altered and disrupted. Working at the time as a global fundraising advisor for the international children's charity SOS Children's Villages International, I was on a daily basis consumed by death – how many people were dying every day in each country globally because of this situation. Then the death of George Floyd happened in Minneapolis and I found myself breaking social distancing rules to go on a Black Lives Matter march in Manchester in early June. Suddenly we were living in a surreal environment that was a combination of the Great Depression and the civil rights movement.

We lost Little Richard during this time, and I spent hours watching YouTube interviews of the most wildly entertaining, yet deeply conflicted, individual in early rock and roll. How was an extravagantly gay black man able to rise to such fame in fifties America? Why did he then renounce rock and roll and turn to religion? We also lost Dave Greenfield of the Stranglers to Covid-19 and I found myself reliving a teenage fascination with a band that snarled and rebelled its way through the late seventies and eighties with very unpolitically correct lyrics.

As rock and roll and death consumed my brain, I put together the combination of short stories and poetry you have in your hands now. Following on from my two previous collections, *I Wasn't Made For These Times* (2004) and *I'm Not Like Everybody Else* (2017), there is an emphasis on misfit characters and an exploration of the duality of achieving success, fame and happiness and also wanting to die. Is happiness a boring concept for talented artists? Do you have to live on the edge to create great art, but also pay the price for this?

The whole history of rock and roll is said to be cursed by a Faustian pact that Robert Johnson created at a crossroads in Mississippi – he sold his soul to the Devil in exchange for the greatest guitar-playing skills. Some argue that this curse was what led to Buddy Holly's plane crash, Eddie Cochran's car crash in Chippenham, Elliott Smith stabbing himself to death in Los Angeles, and all of the legendary '27 Club' deaths that befell Jimi Hendrix, Brian Jones, Jim Morrison, Janis Joplin, Kurt Cobain, Amy Winehouse, etc.

Other people's deaths shape many of the characters in this book. Rock and roll is indelibly marked by watershed moments of tragedy and trauma. And like in normal people's lives, some recover and find new purpose from this and some never bounce back and live out their old age with bitterness and regret. In the midst of my own midlife crisis and a world that was shaking around me, I renewed my strength with the thought that death is not to be feared by someone who has lived right.

JOHNNY PANIC
(FROM A BASEMENT ON THE HILL)

'Poetry is not an expression of the party line. It's that time of night, lying in bed, thinking what you really think, making the private world public, that's what the poet does.'

Allen Ginsberg

I had wanted to interview him for a while. I loved his music and I loved the outsider image he had. Five great solo albums and an interesting career before that in different bands. I didn't know what to expect as I made my way through the jungle to Echo Park and knocked on his door. I knew he lived with a girlfriend, but he had explained over the phone that she would not be in and so it turned out. The two of us sat on the porch, me drinking a coffee, him with just a glass of water. The interview began.

'So were you always destined to be a musician?'

'Well, I don't know about that. I was born in Omaha, Nebraska, but my parents divorced when I was six and I was raised mainly in Texas by my mother and a stepfather. I learnt to play the piano and clarinet at a young age and had musically supportive parents. However, I hated the

1

redneck characters and the mainstream jock culture of Texas. It was like a society that Adolf Hitler would have fantasised about. The popular and successful were the white Aryan sporty kids – the jocks and the cheerleaders, I guess. I changed my name from Steve, because it just sounded too much like a jock name. Also, Steve Smith was the name of the drummer in Journey and they weren't really a favourite band of mine.'

'I can see though that you have a tattoo of the state of Texas on your upper arm?'

'Well I got it when I moved to Portland and I wanted something to symbolise what I had been through in Texas, the whole experience – the nasty characters, the abuse I experienced from my stepfather and the fact that I had escaped to the other side, but was scarred by it. The tattoo symbolises that scarring. I do not love Texas, but you react against cruelty and racism and mainstream teasing in a way that shapes your vulnerability and your songwriting process. In the land of the blind, the one-eyed man is king. Songs like "Some Song," "Flowers for Charlie" and "No Confidence Man," they are about bad experiences I had been through as a kid growing up in Texas. If I had been a happy child, growing up on Long Island with a stable family, I may not have written half the songs I have today.'

I knew at this point that it was too sensitive to delve deeper into his childhood. The abuse from his stepfather I had read about in other interviews and I didn't feel comfortable yet asking him if this abuse was of a sexual nature or not.

'At least in Portland I was away from the bullying characters a bit and I met some kindred spirits. I had some random jobs at first, spreading gravel and transplanting bamboo trees. But I met and fell in with some musicians and some decent people up there – Garrick Duckler and Jason Hornick in particular.'

'So tell me how you came to release your first studio album, *Roman Candle*?'

'Well I was in a band in Portland called Stranger than Fiction, with the guys I just mentioned, but I also studied over in Massachusetts for a few years and then had another band called A Murder of Crows and I called myself Johnny Panic for a while.'

'Ha! Johnny Panic – that is a great rock-and-roll name.'

'Right, we had a lot of cassette tapes in that period but the guys in my next band, Heatmiser, didn't like that name, so I had to drop it. We released a few good albums, but I really wanted to branch out and do something that was totally mine. I wanted a lo-fi album that I could just make on a four-track cassette recorder in my bedroom. I wanted to get as far away from the grunge thing as possible. Something that was just a statement of me and where I was at as a person in my life – really sparse and raw. I had to do a solo record to make that happen. I really loved writing songs and recording them, but I found playing live hard work. I only did it for the sake of promoting the material I had put on the last album, so that my record label wouldn't drop me and I could make a second album and then a third one and so on.'

'You mean to say you don't like playing live?'

'I hate playing on my own in front of an audience. I always get super nervous beforehand, then the gig itself is just a blur. The only thing I enjoy about the whole process is the relief I feel after the gig. But even that only lasts a few hours, because by the next morning the pre-gig terror sets in again. I only enjoy writing and recording music; I wish that was all I could do.'

'So, bearing that in mind, what was it like to play at the Oscars back in 1998?'

'Well it was OK actually. I only played for two minutes and most of the people that were there weren't there to actually see me, so funnily enough I found the overall pressure less intense. Of course, the glamour and glitz of the Oscars isn't really for me, but I guess it was like walking on the moon. It was an OK experience and will never happen to me again.'

We both laughed and broke off the interview to talk a little about California and my journey that day. He seemed like a genuinely nice guy, but he seemed so fragile and vulnerable to me. Did he like the idea of being a famous singer, I asked him, remarking that most kids in America picked up a guitar as a teenager for that very reason.

'I am the wrong kind of person to be really big and famous.'

'What do you mean by that?'

'Well, I mean, I hate playing live and I hate crowds of mainstream people and I hate having lots of attention and spotlight thrown on me. It just makes me think constantly about my worthlessness and the fact that I am empty inside. When I am writing and recording music I am more able to escape that feeling, but that is literally the only time. I have attention deficit hyperactivity disorder and I experience a lot of paranoia when the spotlight is thrown onto me. When I was on the Cavity Search label and even on Kill Rock Stars the balance was just about OK, but after the Oscars I was put on Dreamworks and that was a little too much for me to take at times.'

'So your fourth solo album, *XO* – major label, some mainstream exposure. How were you coping with it all?'

'I was falling apart. I was hating the live gigs and I was hating all the pressure. I tried to kill myself one time in North Carolina by running off the edge of a cliff. And I started taking heroin a lot around this time. I wrote most of that album sitting in the Luna Lounge in New York City at the time. This was an era before 9/11 and there was an abandoned hedonism running through that city – pushed underground a bit maybe by the dancing ban and other dumb things that Mayor Giuliani did. I hung out with some of the Strokes and Interpol at that time, before they had had their breakthrough albums. But I needed the drugs in New York then, to get me through the pain I was feeling in my head. It was somehow as if the moment I received wider public and media exposure, was the moment all the demons from my childhood decided to rise up to the surface and start giving me daily torment. I kept hearing those voices and the voice of my stepfather: "You are no good", "You are a nobody from Nebraska", "Your daddy doesn't love you", "Go down on me."'

We took a fifteen-minute break and I went out to my car and made a short phone call to my girlfriend back in New York. I wanted to know that her day was going OK and that she knew I was doing the interview as planned. When we both reconvened on the porch, I could sense that Elliott's mood had changed and he was displaying panicked arm gestures and movements. His voice too had become stressed and manic. I was not sure what he had done in those fifteen minutes. I started thinking that dark forces were at work. I no longer had control of this interview and he started talking at tangents and displaying painful silences followed by raw bursts of emotion.

'There is this white van that has been following me recently. Did you see it when you were outside on the street?'

I remarked that I hadn't seen a white van and was puzzled as to why anyone would be following him at this time. He was sweating a lot more now and had some wild terror in his eyes.

'Yeah this white van follows me around town and it has been happening for months now. But I struggle to get a good sighting of the driver, so I just speed up all the time to try and lose it. Sometimes it goes away, but often, in the morning, if I head out towards Hollywood or towards the beaches, it will be hot on my tail. People have also been breaking into my house recently. It has happened a few times. Only a few weeks ago they stole a load of recent songs I wrote off my computer.'

'Have you reported this to the police?'

'No. It's no good. It's the record label after me and putting pressure on me for that next big album. The next one that is going to break me really big and make them all a load of money. When I write lo-fi uncommercial music they steal it off me. They are just trying to make me sound like the Beatles, like they did on my last album. I know that the reviews were good and that people like you probably liked it, but honestly I thought it was the most dishonest album I have ever released in my life – just way too much record company interference and it was diluting the messages I was trying to convey.'

I told him that I liked the last album, but that I felt he had mellowed a little from the intensity of previous records. He didn't like this remark and it seemed to strike a nerve. Suddenly the interview was becoming very frenetic and uncomfortable for both of us.

'I haven't been sleeping properly recently and I am only really eating ice cream. I am spending a lot of money on crack and heroin. Hell, if Dreamworks don't release me from my contract I may have to kill myself.'

'Don't do that. I know you have so much more great music to give to the world. Don't you want to be alive to make that happen?'

I felt that appealing to his admitted love of the songwriting and recording process might help him calm down a little and see some sense. I was worried now that the man in front of me was on the edge and in need of a lot of help.

'Also, have you considered getting psychiatric help out here in LA?' I asked.

He didn't respond to this question for a while and then showed me a framed photo of his girlfriend.

'This is Jennifer. She's beautiful, don't you think?'

'Absolutely. And she's a musician too, right?'

'Yeah, she is really talented and inspires me a lot. She knows everything I went through as a child and what my stepfather did to me. You should be interviewing her really...Anyway, I mention her because she has been helping me with all of my addictions and my paranoia. She booked me into the Neurotransmitter Restoration Centre in Beverly Hills to start a course of treatment for substance misuse. I am clean right now and it's thanks to her.'

We both felt a cathartic calm spread across the balcony, and we stopped talking for a while and allowed the refreshing breeze to drift across both of our sweaty faces.

'I can't perform live any more. I hate the way I look and I keep forgetting the words and fucking the songs up. My last gig I just ended up finishing it with 'Long, Long, Long' and that was totally unplanned. Also, I have written the words 'KALI – the destroyer' in permanent ink on my right arm...Anyway, listen, thanks for coming over, but I think that is enough from me for today. Jennifer will be back soon and I don't want you to miss your flight. The traffic from Echo Park to the airport can be a bitch.'

I didn't have to catch a flight, but I didn't want to rock the conversation. It felt like the right time to end our brief interview. I was eternally grateful for meeting him, especially as many of my colleagues had told me that he hated giving interviews and might easily cancel on me at the last minute. It felt like to get this far was a blessing in itself. He agreed to walk out to my car with me.

'Thank you so much for everything, I really appreciate you doing this interview for me. I really want to wish you success with the next album.'

'Thank you. And what you said about me seeking help. I have given up alcohol, meat and sugar this last month. I am on some antidepressants and a few meds, but I am generally OK. I understand your concern for me, I do. You are a good person. But it's hard for another person to know what another human being is going through.'

We embraced and said goodbye to each other. I got into my car and noticed the words 'KALI – the destroyer' on his arm for the first time properly as I put my car into gear and headed down the street. Kali, the Hindu goddess of death, time and doomsday – a mother figure to some people – but heavily associated with sexuality and violence in my brain.

As I drove down Melrose, I wondered about the unsettled and exposed man I had just spent time with. I liked him so much, but I was worried for his future. Would his girlfriend, Jennifer, be able to cope with his mood swings? How was she coping living all alone with him at this time?

I put my favourite record of Elliott's on and thought more about the fickle nature of fame in the United States in the twenty-first century. A lot of people don't want it and can't handle it. His words rang through my brain again and again:

'I am the wrong kind of person to be really big and famous.'

And my favourite song kicked in as I hit the accelerator and headed out towards Venice, and started thinking about the timeline for getting the interview typed out and eventually published. I'm never gonna know you now, but I am gonna love you anyhow.

I BURN TODAY

'I don't have any other message other than don't forget you are alive'

Joe Strummer

I burn today with ideas, words, music and enthusiasm.

Yesterday I had to identify the body of my dead brother on a stretch of grass by the lake in Regent's Park. He had accepted that life was not the way he wanted it and he took an overdose. Although we went to school together and were close as children, we had drifted apart recently. I had been the gobby, confident prankster with a purple heart and he was the quiet, intense follower. He had fallen in with a crowd from the National Front, listened to Enoch Powell speeches and adorned his bedroom with swastikas and right-wing Nazi symbolism. He had to find something to cling to as a code of conduct and he had to have a crowd that could mirror his frustrations. I knew now that I did too.

I was the first person to identify his body and saw him lying there cold after three days. In death he was still a little bit the Scottish heather of my mother and an awful lot the cold distance of my father. He had killed himself by taking a massive overdose of aspirin. Something had to be done to tell the world how he felt. I understood his action. Respected it even.

For my part I am going to fight fascism even harder now. I am going to fight ignorance even harder now. I am going to smash up the Little Englander mentality that engulfed and killed my brother, by celebrating the outsiders and the foreigners. Embracing Jamaican music and embracing South American revolutionary politics, and embracing the highways and music venues of America and Canada and New Zealand and Australia and Thailand and France and Spain and Germany and Italy.

I believe in the cathartic power of the ragged rock-and-roll song. I need to be a man out of time, a drifter, a nomad and fight against everything that the National Front stands for. The immigrant sees the world for what it really is, the oppressed knows the truth and the underdog holds the keys to the kingdom.

All journalists are complete swine and a squatter is making a bold political statement. My brother has just committed suicide and I should feel guilty about this. I saw the decline happening and I did nothing to stop it. I knew about the manipulation going on around him and the forces that drove the racists and the skinhead fanatics into my brother's impressionable brain. As I recoil into myself and cry away from the eyes of the predictable, I vow to change the world for the better and dedicate that change to David.

I am going to put my feet back on that Manhattan turf. I am going to stand on the south-west corner of Tompkins Square Park. After the pandemic there is a new Year Zero. When the whole world falls silent, even one voice becomes powerful. I burn today more brightly than ever before.

EDDIE COCHRAN'S LAST JOURNEY

Gene Vincent and I have just finished a show in Bristol and are heading back to London. The gig went really well – these English kids really understand their rock and roll and go wild for it. I feel like I am bigger over here than I am back home. Back home, it's all Elvis Elvis Elvis. Damn it, I am better than Elvis; I write my own material for a start and I am prepared to tour outside of my own country. You can't just spend all your life playing to crowds in your own country; you gotta take that rock-and-roll energy to the far corners of the planet.

Despite this UK tour going well, I have been bummed out a lot recently. I feel like my career peaked in 1956, when I appeared in the film *The Girl Can't Help It*, singing 'Twenty Flight Rock'. That film was so influential, all the promoters in England kept telling me that. Me, Gene, Little Richard, Fats Domino – we tore up that movie and no one had ever seen the likes of it before. My scene had particular cultural relevance. Whilst I am playing, the white folks, including the beautiful Jayne Mansfield, just stared with their mouths open and with looks of incredulity on their faces. Bless her, but Jayne was not hip to the rock-and-roll sound in 1956. But the African American housekeeper in the scene loves the music and starts dancing to my beat like crazy. And she moved real graciously and elegantly too. Trust me, in 1956 that was a rebellious thing to watch. The African American servant girl connecting with something that her white masters and mistresses did not understand. That upset a few folks watching the movie, but that was the whole point of rock and roll. We wanted to upset the status quo.

Anyway, these country roads out of Bristol are quiet tonight. Gives me a lot of time to think. How can I be bigger than Elvis? What can I do to get a British number-one hit single?

'Hey Gene,' I yell after a long period of quiet in the car, 'What do you think of my new record, "Three Steps to Heaven"?'

'I think it sucks!'

He is just trying to wind me up tonight. We are good friends, but we are not inclined to give each other compliments. To the media and the outside world though we champion each other's music. And in truth we love each other's songs – 'Bluejean Bop' and 'Be-Bop-A-Lula' go round my head every day and get me out of bed in the morning, and the Blue Caps, oh boy, what a great bunch of guys.

Damn it, what does everyone see in those terrible Elvis Presley movies? The guy is just controlled by the Memphis mafia! Gets an army haircut, goes and serves his country like a good ol' boy. That is exactly the attitude that I am rebelling against. I am not about obedience and being shouted at. I am about freedom of expression and cutting

13

loose from the ties of tradition and service. I mean, when 'Skinny Jimmy' was released on Crest Records it didn't sell much, and I had been through a lot of rejection before that too. I had hung out with Connie 'Guybo' Smith in Los Angeles and he played all sorts of instruments – bass, steel guitar, mandolin, you name it! Then I met Hank Cochran (no relation, in case you were wondering) and we played for a while as the Cochran Brothers with no real success. I knew I had to go it alone.

I remember the phone call like it was yesterday. Some dude called Boris Petroff:

'Hey kid, we think you have talent. Do you want to appear in a movie we are making with Jayne Mansfield?'

Why the hell not! I had nothing to lose at that point. I went out the next week to a studio in Los Angeles and laid down versions of 'Twenty Flight Rock' and 'Dark Lonely Street'. This Petroff guy liked what he heard and got 'Twenty Flight Rock' into the movie and with the momentum of that I landed my first record deal with Liberty Records. That song just had smooth chunky wedge chords on the guitar to get you going, a bit of fiddle in the background and my friend Jerry Capehart banging the hell out of a soup carton. The simple sounds are always the best!

My goal in the early days was to be cocky and vulnerable at the same time. That was the ultimate rock-and-roll paradox, right? All of us have that – Buddy Holly, Chuck Berry, Little Richard, Gene Vincent, me…We are tough enough to appeal to the tough boys out there, but we embrace vulnerability and outsider cool and that gets the girls going too, I guess. Well I got a girl with a record machine…

I started singing to myself in the back of the car as we drove further and further away from Bristol and into the English night. I beat my hands on my legs to get the rhythm of the song right.

'Jeannie Jeannie Jeannie' and 'Pretty Girl' didn't sell too great, but then I did 'Summertime Blues', which was a top-ten smash! I am still real proud of that one. It's just got so much rebellion in the lyrics and the singing. Then I did 'C'Mon Everybody', which was a big hit over here in England. Then I did 'Teenage Heaven' and 'Something Else'.

'Hey Gene, I am four years into my chart career and I am tired. I just need one really big hit. How about I take the wheel now?'

'Eddie, you have been drinking. That's not a great idea.'

Our tour manager, Pat, put that idea in its place pretty darn quick. I was starting to get moody and mad in this car with Gene, Pat and my fiancée, Sharon.

'Rock and roll is turning into a nostalgia show, you know! Drive faster, let's see how fast we can go on these country roads.'

'Calm down, baby,' my fiancée said to me.

Sharon was beautiful and I really wanted to marry her, but I was frustrated. I wanted to be bigger than Elvis and I wanted a big hit. We had just played the last show of the tour and were heading back to Heathrow Airport. Gene and I were knocking back some beers in the back seat with Sharon up front and Pat driving.

'Drive faster, Pat! The tour is over, we don't have to follow any darn rules any more. Let's see if this car can take off...'

Gene and I clicked our beers together and started singing each other's songs in the cool spring night with the back windows down. We were all hurtling together through the night and feeling some rock-and-roll rebellion in our veins. We were heading now through an English town called Chippenham.

I am almost happy in this moment. Almost happy. I just gotta figure out what to do now to get myself a British number-one hit single. A number one for all those English boys and girls that had flocked to see me and Gene on this tour that has just ended. Let me know if you have any ideas...

A VIKING ROADIE NO MORE

'I wanted to have the adoration of John Lennon, but have the anonymity of Ringo Starr. I didn't want to be a frontman. I just wanted to be back there and still be a rock-and-roll star at the same time.'

Kurt Cobain

No one saw the washed up body on the beach for a few days. The lockdown had just started, so people were not allowed to venture far out of their houses.

Johnny woke up on a cloudy day in April. He made himself a black coffee with three teaspoons of sugar and walked out to the deserted headland overlooking the English Channel. He had to have fresh air and caffeine early in the day. He had to force himself to get out of bed and do this to stave off the depression he had felt since he hit fifty. He had to look out to the sea early in the morning, otherwise he would feel regret and remorse throughout the rest of the day. He went from the headland to the cottage and back to the headland again. A bachelor always, the little quirks did not need to be justified to anyone else and the deep-grooved behaviour habits kept him satisfied in his loneliness. He used to be a leather-clad rocker, but now he was alone in this world with nobody to share his life. It was going to be sad to die like this, death has no companion, but at least he had the great memories of over twenty years as a roadie to justify his existence on this earth.

Back in the day Johnny was your main man if you were looking for trouble. He specialised in it. He could get you a fix and he had contacts in every town in England pretty much. He had roadied for the U.K. Subs and Anti-Nowhere League. This guy had seen some action.

Looking out to the sea without a job now, Johnny thought about his empty existence. He thought about his childhood on the south coast and his endless relationship with the sea. The sea had been the one constant in his life – a close friend on a weekly basis that he could bounce his troubles off by going on long walks, skimming stones, jumping breakwaters or even going out for a swim. He thought about his school years and then the death of his mother and then his father two years later. He then thought about his reckless years on the road to numb the pain he felt ashamed to show.

Johnny knew that most of his contemporaries had families and were happy now. Most of them had so much to look forward to – their children's successes, their children's careers, partners and then grandchildren. It meant they had something to talk about constantly and life would never be dreary through your fifties. But Johnny had never wanted children. He had never wanted to feel tired from a lack of sleep day after day. He had never wanted to have the constant responsibility for other people's lives; it was hard enough looking after himself he felt.

Tumbling with the tumbleweed. Down the open road. Johnny kept looking out to the calm sea and the grey sky above it. It was 10 a.m. now and the beach was almost deserted on a Tuesday morning. A few dog walkers could be seen in the distance. Johnny sat down with the empty cup of coffee clasped between both hands. There had been one girl once. One girl that could have taken him out of his apathy.

Allison was her name and she had dated one of the drummers in a band that he had worked for when Johnny was in his early thirties. Johnny had never been loved by a woman. No woman had ever slept in his arms with abandon. There was never any triumphant passion or superhuman happiness. There was never a situation where four arms made a single creature.

Allison was so fantastic. She was everybody's favourite little rock and roller at the time. Johnny liked her, but she belonged to another guy that Johnny worked for and liked.

The band was on a long, arduous UK tour one summer back in the nineties and had played all the classic venues of the day:

Barrowlands, Glasgow
Mayfair Ballroom, Newcastle
Cardiff University
The Zodiac, Oxford
Assembly Rooms, Derby
De Montfort University, Leicester
Rock City, Nottingham
Leeds Irish Centre
Manchester Academy
Wolverhampton Civic Hall
Plymouth Pavilions
Cornwall Coliseum

The Opera House Nightclub, Bournemouth
Southampton Guildhall
Portsmouth Guildhall
Shepherd's Bush Empire, London
Cambridge Corn Exchange

A connection had built up between Allison and Johnny as the tour progressed. She attended every gig, as did he, obviously. By the time they hit the Midlands venues, her boyfriend's behaviour was becoming more and more erratic. On stage and in sound checks he held it together well, but after the gigs he was flirting more and more with other girls he met at after-show parties and nightclubs. He was also displaying more and more loose-cannon behaviour and not coming back to the hotel some nights. The band was at the peak of their success and everyone was losing their head a little, as the late nights and the alcohol dominated people's actions.

The boom town was over. A ghost town was all that was left now.

By the time of the Cornwall Coliseum gig, Allison opened up to Johnny down by the sea an hour or so after the sound check.

'Another sell-out hey?'

'Yeah, this is probably the most successful tour I have ever been on,' he responded.

'And we have *TFI Friday* and *Top of the Pops* still to come. Woo hoo,' Allison replied with clear sarcasm.

'You never wished you were in the band?' She asked him as they threw pebbles into the sea in synchronicity.

'Me? No, I hate being on stage. I would get nervous

every day and that would offset any of the enjoyment for me. I hate being the centre of attention. Makes me feel all anxious and tense inside. I like doing my job well and then sitting back and enjoying the show as a punter.'

'That's fair enough,' Allison responded. 'I don't think any of these guys have that problem...'

And she let out a sad laugh. 'Fucking egomaniacs the lot of them.'

'How is it going with Dave?' Johnny asked her, knowing that there was a growing divide between them as the tour had progressed.

'He cheated on me in Nottingham. He spent the night with another girl that he met in the Cookie Club after the gig. He told me he didn't actually have sex with her and that he passed out too drunk, but I don't really believe him. We argued a lot for a few days and we haven't slept together since. I don't really know why I am still on the road with everyone to be honest. I should probably go back and live with my mum in Brighton.'

Johnny consoled Allison with a hug and told her that he thought Dave was an ungrateful asshole and didn't deserve such a great girlfriend. He stopped short of telling her she deserved better and labouring the point, because he felt some loyalty to the band and considered them to be his mates.

Allison put her head against his shoulder and they kept throwing pebbles into the sea. Allison was beautiful, with her brunette hair and red highlights, and her rock-and-roll dress sense. Her heroin-chic figure made her the nearest thing to a Kate Moss rock-and-roll girlfriend that he had witnessed close up.

'When this tour is all over, I am going to study to be a nurse at the University of Sussex and forget all about Dave. You should come and see me in Brighton some time. I know you only live up the coast.'

Johnny remembered looking at his watch and telling Allison that they should go back to the concert venue, as the support band would be starting soon. As they both stood up, she kissed him on the lips and squeezed him tightly.

'I would be much better off with a guy like you, wouldn't I? You should have more confidence in yourself. You are a gentle giant and you look like a Viking. A lot of girls like that, you know...'

Johnny should have had more confidence with himself, but he didn't because he was always surrounded by rock stars and guys who had every reason for total self-confidence. He carried equipment round, drove vehicles, set up amplifiers and mike stands and tuned guitars. That was all he ever did and it fed him no confidence or self-esteem. So he never followed up on the kiss on the pebble beach, but just put his head down, did his job and stayed loyal to his employers. For a few days Allison gave him suggestive looks in the moments that their eyes met, but this soon faded as she began to realise that any attempt at seduction would be in vain.

The tour continued until its *Top of the Pops* conclusion that August, but Allison left the tour bus after the Portsmouth gig and went back to live with her mum. Soon after this, Dave told Johnny that they had split up and that he had a new girlfriend, a model that he had met after a gig on the previous year's tour. No one ever mentioned

Allison again and Johnny never saw her again, although he often thought of that evening sat on the pebbles in Cornwall. He worked hard at his trade and let apathy take over his thought processes with women. The attractive girls all wanted to be with the guys in the bands, the guys that were on the stage. None of them wanted to get with a roadie; he was wise to that, so he gave up all intention or desire for a long-term partner.

At a point below zero
There's no place left to go.

Johnny stood up now on the headland and walked back into his house. The days had been monotonous recently during the lockdown. The only excitement he got from life was driving fast around country roads in his clapped-out old car and putting on his favourite vinyl records loudly in his house, and jumping around the living room playing air guitar and air drums. There was literally nothing else to live for. Johnny had nothing and he was beginning to hear the hound dogs on his trail.

But on this particular Tuesday morning, something stirred inside of him. Even he had grown tired of the apathy. Even he had grown tired of the loneliness. He decided within himself that he was going to try to track down Allison, the girl that he had shared that one moment of excitement with around twenty years ago. There was social media out there now, and he had a Facebook profile, so he could try to track her down this way. He spent most of the afternoon looking for her on Facebook. She would be in her late forties now, he thought, probably married with children and probably with a different last name. She was tough to track down, but he found an

Allison that was a mutual friend with one of the other roadies that had been on that tour at the time as well. He sent the friend request from his computer and sat and watched the screen. He put on a few of his favourite albums from that era and poured himself a Jack Daniels. As the evening wore on, he kept looking at his Facebook to see if the friend request had been accepted, but there was no response. The Allison he had requested had a profile picture of a beach and the sea, but nothing else, and this gave him some hope.

Days passed and there was no response to his friend request. He started typing in different combinations to find her and sending off other friend requests in desperation:

Allison, Brighton
Allison, Sussex
Allison, Worthing
Allison, nurse
Allison, NHS

But nothing came up that gave him any hope.

All these southern girls are all the same.

After a week had passed, Johnny abandoned his search and resigned himself to defeat. It was no good. No good could come from this, he thought. He even had a dream one night that he did track her down and went to her house in Brighton. There was excitement in the dream. But when he knocked on the door, a man opened it and proclaimed himself to be Allison's husband and that Allison was working late that night at the hospital. The husband lingered awkwardly at the doorway for a while as

Johnny became tongue-tied. Two teenage children could be heard talking loudly in the hallway behind him.

'I have to go now, mate,' the husband told Johnny in the dream. 'I am taking these two to see Ed Sheeran tonight. I will tell Allison you called though; what was your name again?'

'It doesn't matter,' Johnny responded, 'but thank you for your kindness. Enjoy the Ed Sheeran concert.'

Johnny woke up. He knew that it had just been a dream, but the fear of a similar reality happening if he tried to indulge his Allison obsession any further gripped him and he walked slowly into his kitchen.

This sadness never ceases.

Johnny made his habitual morning coffee with three sugars and walked out onto the headland once again in his dressing gown. Barefooted, he walked down onto the beach, utterly crushed by the dream he had just had. He walked straight ahead towards the sea, striding through the morning rain without thinking of how he might look to a passer-by. He walked knee deep into the cold English Channel, which was slightly nearer to low tide that morning, but not all the way out. He looked up and wondered whether the same grey sky above him also rained down on Allison and her happiness in another part of the country. He turned left and walked on through the saltwater, as if driven by some strange instinct. He had a moment with Allison that could have built into something incredible. But his lack of self-confidence and self-esteem had blighted him. He was tired of being alone, but it was all too late now. In his fifties, his health was failing him; any good looks he had once possessed were gone from him forever. His dressing gown was now soaked and he threw the empty mug he was holding deep into the sea. After ten minutes of walking through the waves like this, he turned right and started walking deeper into the sea and then swimming when his feet could not touch the ground. Johnny made it his mission to keep swimming deeper and deeper into the English Channel until he could swim no more. The cold of the water was chilling his entire body and he was weeping and crying out at the sea with no purpose.

And Johnny kept on swimming.

And Johnny kept on swimming.

And Johnny kept on swimming.

I PEAKED IN 1989

'This Polish lady, I thought to myself, was the type and the genius of deep crime. I saw how she refused to be alone. And then I felt relieved of my midlife crisis. I did want to grow up. This lady was the woman of the crowd. It would have been in vain to keep following her. I wouldn't have learnt any more about her if I followed her for eternity, and I wouldn't have learnt any more about myself.'

These were Hanif's final words to me as I finished interviewing him, and then he left me and walked away into the Manhattan evening.

I had been a journalist most of my professional life, and the opportunity to interview a literary god, now well into his seventies and semi-retired, but with a back catalogue of ten bestselling novels, five plays, six short-story collections and countless essays and journalistic achievements of his own, was an opportunity I relished.

I met him in a tea shop in the East Village, one block away from Tompkins Square Park. Physical Graffitea it was called and was in the building of the famous 1975 Led Zeppelin album front cover. I had haunted the East Village most of that sticky and claustrophobic summer. I had been single for a while, my health had been poor and in many ways my life was feeling like a slow-motion car crash. I knew I was in the midst of dealing with turning forty and trying to shed my old skin in metamorphosis. Maybe the Hanif interview could help jolt me out of this.

I showed up wearing a denim shirt and a stars-and-stripes bandana round my neck. I would have looked cool back in a small city in the UK. In New York, with its dazzling displays of hipster diversity, I don't think anyone had noticed my presence since daylight.

Hanif was dressed in a grey ensemble, matching the greying hair and the greying skin. He was ghost-like and rugged – mid-sixties maybe, but he could have been older. His presence at the interview table immediately took me back in time. Phone switched off. Recording switched on. I immersed myself in his movements, his gestures and his words. I loved the interview process.

'I used to like St Mark's Place,' Hanif started with. 'I wrote a story in Bull McCabes one time. But I hand-wrote it and I lost the notepad. I have never tried to rewrite it. A lover I had in the late nineties stole the damn manuscript off me. We had an intense argument one morning and as a result I lost many of my possessions. I can't remember if the lover was male or female. My writing at the time was like Robert Frost's definition of a poem – a structure of words that consumes itself as it unfolds, like ice melting on a stove...'

'What is your favourite part of the East Village?' he asked me. I told him I liked the tea shop we were sat in right now because I was obsessed with Led Zeppelin as a teenager. And we talked about 'Bron-Yr-Aur', the seventies folk music scene and then a little of Robert Plant's solo work.

'My favourite Robert Plant album,' Hanif told me, 'is *Mighty ReArranger* from 2005. He had a great band then called the Strange Sensation and I feel like it was the first time that he had made something that matched up to his Led Zeppelin years.'

We agreed and we also acknowledged that this started a golden period for Robert – leading to the reunion concert, the *Raising Sand* album and the *Band of Joy* album.'

'So, what do you consider to be your peak as a writer?' I asked him. In the late eighties and early nineties, two of his novels had captured the literary zeitgeist and he was considered on a par with Martin Amis and Roddy Doyle.

'I think the novel I wrote in 1989 was my best. It was my coming-of-age book and it led to my golden period through the nineties. I had wanted to be a writer since I was a teenager in London. I had grown up with all the classic conflicts of a British Asian boy at that time. I felt no connection to my parents' religion, their motherland or the culture they had been raised in and still clung to. I was obsessed with the counter-culture, the burgeoning rock music and punk music scenes around me and the excitement of illegal drugs and sexual encounters. To throw on top of that, I knew I was bisexual, but I knew I couldn't talk about this to anyone. I slept with my first man at a house party with the Pink Floyd album *Ummagumma* playing in the background. I walked home the next morning through London streets, feeling liberated. When I saw my parents later that day, I felt internal confusion and buried everything. I wanted men, but I dated girls. I took all the illegal drugs I could get hold of and devoured books and music with wild abandon. I wrote lots of articles and short stories at this time. But none of them were any good. I created no art of note in my twenties or early- and mid-thirties. I just lived fast and hard and fucked anything I could. I was a writer and I needed fresh experience. I wanted to be like Ginsberg or Kerouac. My heroes through the eighties were the Beat writers and Joe Orton and Prince and Baudelaire. They were rivers of talent and I fed off them, but my own art was vacuous.'

The Manhattan daytime heat was sultry and we both ordered two more iced teas and stared for a while at the yellow taxis and the street hustlers outside. I hadn't figured out how to hustle in New York yet, but hustle was all around me. I knew my own clock was ticking, my time on this earth limited and Hanif's words made me feel that I too had let my twenties and thirties be a torrent of hedonism. I knew that I was part of the crowd now in New York and I desperately wanted to not be part of the crowd.

'How old are you?' Hanif asked me.

'Forty-one,' I replied.

And then there was no conversation for a while and the greying wizard breathed deeply and prepared himself for the meaty part of the interview.

'You know that Billy Joel recorded the video for "A Matter of Trust" on this street back in the eighties? Are you old enough to remember that?'

I said I didn't know. I wasn't a big Billy Joel fan. He was playing night after night at the Garden these days and I had been told it was a New York rite of passage that you had to go, but I had been unable to score tickets. 52nd Street,

'New York State of Mind'. I had not felt in a New York state of mind all year. It was like I was edging. It was like I was experiencing a ruined orgasm. Thoughts of suicide were flashing across my mind and Hanif, I felt, was only able to distract me for so long.

'And Paul McCartney appeared as an uncredited extra in the Billy Joel video. Not many people know that but me…Watch the video.'

I turned on my phone and we watched the YouTube video of 'A Matter of Trust' from *The Bridge* album together, and sure enough there was a character who looked very much like a *Frog Song*-era Paul McCartney in one of the shots.

'The beauty,' Hanif whispered, 'is in the uncertainty. I wrote many of my best short stories in my forties, when I was your age and a little older. It was the period when I realised I was too old to party hard, take drugs forever and sleep with as many people as possible. But I wasn't old yet and all the same desires were still there. There was just this uncertainty. Like I had the desires, but I didn't know if I had the action. Do you believe that it is Paul McCartney in that video? Neither of us know, do we…My early forties was my sweet spot of uncertainty, experience and work rate. I threw myself in and this was when I wrote my best stuff.'

We then mutually decided to walk out onto St Mark's Place and down to Tompkins Square Park, past Clash City Tattoos, past Doc Holliday's Honky Tonk Bar and across to the Joe Strummer mural emblazoned with 'Know Your Rights' and 'The Future Is Unwritten'. I told Hanif a little about my unease and my unhappiness of the last year and he told me about his singleton life and his desire to write one more great novel before he died. His writing was his anchor, he told me. I told him that I hadn't had an anchor since I turned forty.

'My bestselling works were in the late eighties and nineties and I won a Whitbread Prize and was nominated for a Booker and a Pulitzer, not that I care a great deal for those rewards. For me, the biggest thing now is to go out on a high.'

We went and sat at the bar at Jesse Malin's Niagara and I stopped recording the conversation. Hanif asked the waitress for two napkins and two pens and totally charmed her with his roguish nature. He had slept with more men than women in his life, he told me, but his charm and charisma seemed universal. I felt envy at his gravitas, at his retained good looks and at the fact that he had been alive in London in the late seventies, and immersed himself in the punk-rock scene of the Sex Pistols and the Clash. I knew that I could never be as great as Hanif. But perhaps I could get an interview with him published that would do justice to the man.

With the two napkins he challenged me to write two lists:

One of great artists with long careers that managed to achieve great things artistically in their last five years.

The other: a list of my regrets in life to date. He left me and went for a walk down Avenue A and told me I had fifteen minutes to complete the assignment and that it should form a key part of the interview I intended to publish.

I sat motionless at the bar in Niagara for five minutes,

thinking hard and then I threw myself into the list writing in a stream-of-consciousness attack.

List One:
- Johnny Cash
- David Bowie
- Charles Dickens
- Vincent van Gogh
- Edgar Allan Poe
- Leonard Cohen

List Two:
- I had never made a relationship with a woman successful beyond two years.
- I had lost contact with my father after a heated row in my teens.
- Although I had had journalistic successes in magazines, I was yet to write a book that was successful.
- I had broken up with Kay Aspey after six months through impatience. She was a goddess; I could have made that one work!
- I was having a prolonged midlife crisis and I wanted to get out of it. Too many people had told me I was too old for the hedonism now and I needed to settle down.
- I was slipping back into the crowd…

Hanif returned to the bar at Niagara and we sat and continued the interview. We never spoke again about the lists. It was as if that exercise was just for my own self-reflection.

The fresh air on Avenue A had clearly given Hanif a bolt of adrenaline. Now, more than ever, he was happy, dauntless and sagacious. I asked him about his literary heroes and influences and he talked eloquently of the Beat Generation and the great American writers before them – of Hemingway and Faulkner, Nathaniel Hawthorne even. He touched on the great A Level English teacher he had had that raised the bar in his reading habits and his ability to analyse literary techniques and masterstrokes. I too had had such a mentor in my teens, and for ten minutes we bonded further over this and the impact it had had on both our lives. Without these unsung heroes, neither of us would have had the stimulus to pursue a full-time career as a writer.

As the afternoon wore on, I saw more and more similarities between myself and Hanif. I realised that my midlife crisis could potentially be ended the way that Hanif's had. The drug-taking and the partying and the one-night stands could subside and lead to a wiser beginning and a burst of relevant and visceral creativity.

'So, what was it in the late eighties that made you focus more and made you a better writer? Why suddenly did you start writing works that were so much more powerful than before?'

Hanif's mood changed and he became sombre.

'It was this Polish lady that I saw once in a crowded street in London. It was a summer evening, not unlike this one, and I saw this long-blonde-haired lady in her thirties near to the Archway Tube stop in north London. Near to the Archway Tavern, where the Kinks were photographed on the front cover of their *Muswell Hillbillies* album. I had been drinking in the pub on my own. You know the area?'

I nodded. I had known the area well in a former debauched and estranged life.

'I watched her talking to a lady on the wide pavement outside the main Tube entrance and I became infatuated with her beauty. I know a little Polish, so was able to pick up snippets of her conversation. She then walked onto the Tube and I followed her at a distance. On her own, she took the Northern line into central London and I continued to follow her through the streets of Soho. I was weak for her beauty. I could feel her sexuality swaying in the summer evening's breeze, but I needed to keep my distance. I knew I was stalking her, but I didn't know why. At times she stopped and read street signs and at other times she lost herself in the crowded London evening. After half an hour, I knew she had no destination, no fixed purpose, and I could see that she was more lost than me. She was walking through the streets for the sake of walking through the streets. She was a story inside a story inside a story.

'And then it all hit me. This woman was able to hypnotise me completely and I would have followed her around London all summer and eventually been arrested as her stalker. Her mystery and my imagination had the potential to collide with deadly results.'

Hanif looked out at the bright blue Manhattan sky and sighed deeply.

'I followed the Polish lady all night. She was beautiful, voluptuous, lonely, brave, scared – a beating pulse in London's vibrant body of 1989. She had total control over me that night. I followed her eventually until she walked into a doorway on Old Compton Street, but before she walked inside, she turned around and looked at me, as if aware for a moment that she was being stalked. She called me over to her and I obeyed. She was probably in her mid-thirties and her English had a heavy eastern-European accent to it.

"'I need a man," she said. "My son is ill. My son is dying. Will you be that man for me?" "What is your name?" I asked her. "Anna," she replied.

'And for the next few months I lived with Anna and helped support her son. I supported her financially and I talked with her into the early hours of every morning. Our conversations were not deep and they were not revealing, but they soothed us both at that time in our lives.

'I wrote nothing at all in that period. I just based my daily routine around emotionally and financially supporting this lady on Old Compton Street through a difficult period of her life. I never made love to her. In fact, the early sexual attraction I had felt quickly subsided when it became obvious to me that I was there to help this lady. Her son, Boleslav, had a rare cancer and was receiving regular treatment at Great Ormond Street Hospital. Every week he needed treatment, and I would provide the transportation to and from the hospital and the emotional support that mother and son needed. Anna cooked my meals for me and I financially supported her and her son through their dark times. I still had free time to walk the city streets, to shop for CDs on Berwick Street and meet up with friends, but I did so knowing I was helping something bigger than my career or my selfish existence in the world.

'This lifestyle continued for three months in 1989, but then stopped abruptly.

'I came home to Anna's flat on Old Compton Street one evening with some bags of shopping for myself, Anna and Boleslav. Anna was standing at the doorway to her flat entrance.

'"Hanif, you have been very kind to me and I will always be grateful for the love and support you have given to my son and I. He is recovering well now from the cancer."

'I didn't know what to say and handed Anna the shopping bags as the decadent men of Soho walked past us.

'"But now you must leave us. My husband is returning from Poland tomorrow and I must return to my former life and former profession in this area of London. It would not be fair for you to become involved in this work. It has danger for you. Your life must go now in another direction. Boleslav and I will be fine."

'I said that I understood her choices and we embraced and said goodbye to each other. I walked away in the direction of the Paul Raymond Revuebar. She had never told me she was married. I felt cheated initially, but that feeling soon subsided. I realised it was time for me to move on from this period of almost self-isolation. I started writing heavily again and in the following six months I wrote *The Buddha of Suburbia*. In powerfully documenting my first forty years on this earth, I had achieved the success I had always craved and my midlife crisis was finally over. *The Buddha of Suburbia* propelled me to stardom. It was even made into a TV series and David Bowie wrote an acclaimed soundtrack album to it.'

Our interview was drawing to a close now and I paid the bar bill and thanked Hanif for his time. We discussed the follow-up process and I arranged a call with his agent for the following week.

'I am going to die soon,' he told me, 'but I want to write one great novel before I go and that will mean that I leave this world with a satisfied mind. My advice to you though is that you need a Polish-woman moment. A time where you focus for a few months on something completely separate from your career, completely separate from your physical appearance and completely separate from your ego. And get out of New York. I can see it in your eyes that you hate this place and that you need somewhere new to find your anchors in life.'

He got up to leave the Niagara bar, which was now filling up with early-evening artists and musicians.

'Go find your Anna. This Polish lady, I thought to myself, was the type and the genius of deep crime. I saw how she refused to be alone. And then I felt relieved of my midlife crisis. I did want to grow up. This lady was the woman of the crowd. It would have been in vain to keep following her. I wouldn't have learnt any more about her if I followed her for eternity and I wouldn't have learnt any more about myself.'

SWEET HITCH-HIKER

'Everyone I like is either dead or not feeling very well.'
                                                    Tom Waits

It's fun to be alive. It's a hell of a lot better than being dead. I decided to do the road trip on my own because I need to filter the bad thoughts out of my mind. I had a case full of old CDs – all ideal for driving to – Bruce Springsteen's first seven albums, Johnny Cash's prison albums and a lot of old folk music and Americana.

I wanted to start off in Nashville, Tennessee. I visited the Country Music Hall of Fame and spent two days migrating along the bars on Broadway – Layla's, Tootsie's, Legends. Being British born and raised, I knew less than I should have done about country music. As long as it wasn't overly religious, ridiculously patriotic or displaying a right-wing/Republican stance, then I gave it a chance. I liked Hank Williams III, Townes Van Zandt, the Dixie Chicks and Kacey Musgraves in particular. And I bought some outlaw stuff for the drive south too. Freedom is just another word for nothing left to lose.

On Wednesday morning I hit the road for Memphis

with a plan to get to New Orleans by the following Monday. The worries of my job were out of my mind now and my rented Mustang had a great sound system. First up, as I left the Nashville suburbs and haircuts and drove past the Acropolis, was *Darkness on the Edge of Town*, then *The River*, both sides of it, then some Paul Westerberg, 'Dirty Diesel', then Deer Tick and the Gourds. Then back to some more mainstream country and the Dixie Chicks and the corny, yet magnificent, 'Travellin' Soldier'. Then *Flyin' Shoes* by Townes and I think I played the first track, 'Loretta', nine times back to back before allowing the rest of the album to breathe.

This girl had really fucked up my head. I knew that I needed a road trip on my own with lots and lots of music to put me at peace with the world again.

The part of the road trip that I was most excited about was the drive down Highway 61 to the famous crossroads near Clarksdale. The crossroads that Cream had sung about on *Wheels of Fire* and that Jimmy Page and Robert Plant had romanticised on their *Walking into Clarksdale* album. I knew that many decades earlier, the first great bluesman Robert Johnson was supposed to have made a Faustian pact at these crossroads – he was reputed to have sold his soul to the Devil in exchange for incredible guitar-playing skills. If true, it started a chain reaction of events. Robert Johnson was killed by drinking from the poisoned bottle given to him by a man whose wife he had seduced. The Devil played his first hand. Then the bad events started to escalate and escalate, leading to my own traumas and the things that Anita had done to me.

Soon after rock and roll exploded in the fifties and every conservative family in the western world became worried about the souls of their daughters and sons, Lucifer laughed his way through talent after talent.

Buddy Holly died in a devastating air crash in February 1959. Chuck Berry was arrested and thrown in prison for transporting an underage girl across state lines, for immoral purposes. Jerry Lee Lewis married his fourteen-year-old cousin and lost the plot entirely. Little Richard found God and abandoned music completely for a while. Elvis Presley was drafted into the army for two years and John Lennon claimed that he was never the same afterwards – his rebel spirit diluted by having to follow orders from halfwits. And then the late, great Eddie Cochran died in a car crash in Chippenham after a show in Bristol. 'Three Steps To Heaven' topped the British charts and the spirit of rock and roll lay dormant for a while, until the Beatles released their first devastating album in 1963.

I drove fast to get down to those crossroads, believing that the Devil might be there waiting for me and I wanted to see what kind of impact he could have on me.

I had put on Hank Williams III's *Damn Right, Rebel Proud* album and just listened to the song 'Candidate for Suicide', when I first saw the hitch-hiker.

It was around noon and the road was quiet. I had not spoken a word all day.

I like to pick up a hitch-hiker if I can. It's a minor thing and I am a minor king. There was plenty of space in my Mustang and I needed to talk to someone. He looked a little younger than me – late twenties, perhaps. One big backpack on his back and tanned and Hispanic-looking.

'Where you going, buddy?'

'Memphis. Can we make that work?'

'Yeah sure, we can make that work. Jump in. I am Richard from England.'

'Manuel from Puerto Rico.'

'Pleased to meet you, Manuel from Puerto Rico.'

He didn't smile or give out any friendly signals and he got in the back seat of my car. I felt like I instantly trusted this stranger in the sweltering August heat though. The azure blue sky watched down on my car and the dirt roads beckoned me south. Time passed without an apology and I continued driving to Memphis fast – faster than before as if I had a date with something perilous lined up.

For the first hour the conversation between Manuel and I was sporadic and disjointed. His English was limited and he sometimes didn't answer my questions at all. I wasn't bothered by it though. I trusted Manuel, but he seemed distant.

I told him about my life in England and my career. I explained I was on a journey of self-discovery after a messy break-up with a girl in Manchester. He didn't seem that interested. He told me he was hitch-hiking from Chicago to Memphis and sleeping rough most of the time. Life was hard in his country, he said, but he could visit relatives in America and have new adventures. I asked him if he had a girlfriend or wife and he didn't answer.

I let Manuel rummage through my CDs on the back seat and pick one that he liked. He chose a Creedence Clearwater Revival album called *Bayou Country* and I put it on and talked a bit about all my Highway 61 fantasies and my excitement at the hallowed roads we were going to be travelling. Then I let John Fogerty play on without any further conversation between us.

Manuel was handsome, but looked troubled, like he was on the run from something. I noticed through my rear-view mirror that he was twitching from time to time and seemed to like to look closely at the drivers of other cars that passed us.

As we approached the outskirts of Memphis and just when I thought our conversation was running dry, Manuel initiated a strange conversation.

'Did you ever have a Tiger Woman, Richard?'

'A Tiger Woman? Not exactly sure what you mean by that?'

'A woman who is really beautiful, but just wants to hurt you. Did you ever have that?'

'I tend to fall for crazy women. I find them more exciting. The madness and danger is hypnotic, right?'

'Not for me. Not anymore. I am done with that shit. In my country half the girls are like that. How many women did you fuck? In your life – how many?'

'I never kept count, but I think around forty. You?'

'Over two hundred,' and he laughed out the next line as if rehearsed, 'but I am done now. No more for me.'

'So we are travelling this road together to escape something, right?'

Manuel didn't answer, but he had my mind racing now.

'Is there one particular crazy woman you are escaping from? Like I am?' I asked him with more conviction than my other questions.

'There are some things in my life I must never go back to. Maybe you have in your car now, Richard, a murderer...a psychopath...or maybe both.'

Manuel expected me to be scared by this last sentence, but I wasn't. I had done very bad things in my life too, things that no one knew about except for me. I had done things that I had buried deep inside of me, things that Robert Johnson or Jerry Lee Lewis could have sung about with anonymity and mystery, and rock-and-roll writers like Lester Bangs or Charles Shaar Murray would have obsessed over due to the Faustian pact. Talking to Manuel opened up my own wounds and they needed opening.

'So who did you kill?' I asked him.

'Many people,' he replied. 'But they all deserved to die. They were all honourable murders.'

I understood what he meant and didn't feel judgemental.

'In my country, when you fuck more than two hundred people, some will be crazy, some will want revenge and some will tell vicious lies about you to feed their own egos. I don't think I will live for much longer now. This, Richard, is why I am watching the faces of the other drivers – I know you sensed that – watching for the police, watching for my enemies. But I want to get to Memphis, and I want to get to Beale Street tonight. I am meeting one of those crazy Tiger Women there.'

Suddenly, my recent women-troubles seemed fairly tame and I was envious of this Puerto Rican hitch-hiker on my back seat. He had no money, his clothes were dishevelled and he didn't smell great, but his life was alive with danger and jeopardy and I wanted to be him. I wanted that thunder and lightning in my life.

John Fogerty sang 'Proud Mary', and as we headed

off the main highway and followed signs to Downtown Memphis, Manuel suddenly told me he wanted to get out.

'Richard, your life and your job in England is safe. Don't have any Eddie Cochran car crashes and watch out for the Tiger Women. I must get out of the car now.'

And that was that, close to a turning with a Taco Bell and a Subway sandwich joint, the murderer hauled his backpack out of my car and walked away. No 'Thank you for the ride', no parting handshake; he just walked to the other side of the road and was gone.

I made it to the crossroads later that evening. I parked my car with the headlights on as the darkness began to fall.

Robert Johnson was poisoned for sleeping with a married woman. I had slept with many. North of no south. Would my life ever be grounded? I wanted to be like the hitch-hiker. I wanted more life events to run away from. Jimi Hendrix said that the reason he felt so free was that he was always running. I needed to tell people everything I had done. I needed to unleash the beast in me.

I fell down to my knees at the crossroads in Clarksdale and I prayed that the Lord make a decision on me – I wanted to be taken out of my midlife malaise and put in a prison cell with a pen and a notepad. Feed me enough to keep me alive. Bring all the Tiger Women in day after day to torment me. Bring a priest to hear my confession and then leave me alone in the cell for eternity – the albatross always lingering overhead and the uncertainties always real.

COMA GIRL AND THE EXCITEMENT GANG

'Punk rock isn't something you grow out of. Punk rock is an attitude, and the essence of that attitude is "give us some truth".'

Joe Strummer

'Drink this, it will make you feel fabulous.'

Outside the Viper Rooms on the Sunset Strip, there was a feeling of Halloween danger in the air. River told me that he hadn't even wanted to come out that night and was close to staying in. His brother was still underage and Samantha was going to take him along; however, he changed his mind at the last minute and ran to the elevator in their apartment block. Excitedly, he told them he did want to go to the show after all. He wasn't officially a part of the band, but he would likely get invited up to play with everyone. He turned to me, his old school friend of fourteen years, with crazed eyes and long brown hair flailing in the cool evening breeze. Like in that moment that a goose lays a golden egg, he blurted it all out at once:

'Rain doesn't understand our relationship, neither does Liberty, Joaquin or Summer – none of them will ever understand the tragedy. Imagine being called John

Lee Bottom? My father has upset my belief, hope, poetry, fantasy, destroyed my aspirations, ravaged my confidence, killed my love, overthrown the idealistic cult of manhood, murdered the illusions of the heart and altogether performed the most gigantic sceptical operation ever carried out. He has riddled everything with his mockery and drained my body and brain to the arid terrain of the Mojave Desert!'

It was hard to fire a comeback to that. He sounded like the gay hustler he had once played so well, but I knew that character wasn't the real him, far from it. When you spend your life acting and acting, I guess you lose perspective of who you really are and you have to find anchors in your family and your roots. Acting is like a Halloween mask you put on.

I nodded and took extra-long drags of my cigarette. I had been drinking in Rock & Reilly's for a few hours beforehand and the night lay out in front of us. Our friend's band was just about to play an uneven but exciting set inside the Viper Rooms. I left River out on the strip and went inside, as I owed a favour to my Asian girlfriend, Candy, who had been pole dancing and photographing the scene that year. The stars were visible in the Los Angeles sky and River's father had fucked him up beyond compare. No previous attempts I had made to calm him down were going to work tonight. He could only help himself by escaping the scene and self-isolating in a little house in the countryside, maybe by the sea. As I walked back inside the Viper Rooms' main door, I saw River talking to himself on the strip. There was nobody home. There was nobody left to write poetry. Eventually the band came on and I ordered a beer and talked a little to Candy about future projects we would both be involved in. She lived in Santa Monica and I was based in Koreatown at the time; we hadn't moved in together yet. Thank God for the certainty of future artistic projects to keep us both in check from our temptations and vices. We would both make it through the maelstrom, but the storm was getting closer and the waves were getting high. It was the last week of October and we had just started our romantic relationship, but had kept the news between the two of us. I was only twenty-three, still starting out in my career and naïve to the perils of gossip and tabloid scrutiny. Our mutual friend had just returned from Utah and was completing filming on a project called *Dark Blood*, whilst staying at John Frusciante's house. We were all still close, although I was giving my weeks more structure and routine than the people around me, something instilled into me by the military background in my family. Everyone needs a bit of Republican in them to get through this mad and messed-up life, even if we keep it to ourselves most of the time.

I wore a black armband for a year after my friend died. I have also been a vegan and an animal rights activist all my life since. So has Candy. Candy slept with River before she slept with me, but it is OK now, these things don't matter in the long run. We eventually settled down and moved on with our lives and careers, had children, became more centrist in our politics, but never shed the guilt and pain of our friend's overdose. All those 'what ifs' – he should have stayed at my place in Koreatown; I wish I had talked to him more about his father, helped him find some peace with that situation. The guilt never fully goes

48

away, but you have to get outside of your own headspace or you just go round in circles. Our friend made a big mark on this world in a short space of time, but he wasn't meant to be here long. He never would have made that pragmatic move to the centre and I am glad of that. He died young and his idealism has been crystallised.

Nearly sixteen years passed and I sat on the floor with Candy and our eldest boy in the Leftfield tent at Glastonbury Festival. This was Billy Bragg's own curated little festival and a chance for all of us middle-of-the-roaders to relive our idealistic youths. Candy was at ease as a mother now and our boy had been raised on our respective music tastes and ideals. We drank fruit cider, wore straw hats, listened to Billy play lesser-known Woody Guthrie songs and invite speakers onto the stage to engage us with tales of CND, Red Wedge and the imminent downfall of the *Sun*'s Page 3 girls. We had lived all over the world by this point and a jaded music writer and his photographer wife soaked up the uniquely English atmosphere around us.

We were a long way from Los Angeles now, but the type of characters who inhabited East Hollywood or Los Feliz bookstores were also likely to sit in Billy Bragg's Leftfield tent at Glastonbury Festival and escape the mainstream poisons that were so close by.

'I still think about that night at the Viper Rooms every day,' Candy told her friend, who was at the festival as a photographer that year too.

Sitting on the grass and waiting for the next Billy Bragg set, I listened to my wife tell the story of sixteen years previously. The darkest moments in life were only junctures that led to somewhere better. We had all lost someone we had understood. I listened to the story with eyes closed and the big screen in my head. All around me people drank their dark poisoned fruits and the green grass I was sitting on smelled of its colour.

'River was still so young. We were all just twenty-three at the time and it felt like we were all just in love with each other. The scene that we were in was like a mentor that embraced and indulged our pure and naïve loves.

'A lot of the guys were smoking crack, or injecting cocaine intravenously and then injecting heroine. Los Angeles was rife with that stuff at the time. I don't think it is like that anymore.

'Anyway, his last girlfriend, Samantha, was there with him that night and she had some attitude towards me, because I had history with River. I felt there were dirty looks and an undercurrent of bitchiness pointed in my direction. So, I floated around that night and just took pictures. I didn't want to get stuck in an awkward conversation or talking to the wrong person. I didn't like Samantha at all. River, on the other hand, was as beautiful and charming as always that night. He and my husband had been talking a little out on the strip earlier in the night. He had seemed a little high perhaps, but not uncomfortably so. Flea was there that night, Johnny Depp was lurking by the stage and Gibby Haynes of the Butthole Surfers was in the band that night too. It was an awesome place to be a freelance photographer. I was in love with my job that night.'

To give this some perspective, in 1993 and always, Candy had the bad-girl looks and tattoos that made her the object of many a Los Angeles scenester's sexual fantasies. As a music photographer she had plenty of offers. My own insecurities about being her new boyfriend were definitely there that night. They have become diluted over the years, but they could always rise up at times when the early years were discussed in depth. Leaving Los Angeles in the late nineties had been a must-do decision to protect our fragile marriage in its early days. Did Johnny Depp ever fuck my wife? I mean, he owned the Viper Rooms at the time. I never asked her, but I don't think so…

'The thing about the scene at that time is that all of the important artists had lost someone in their lives. It was that loss that made them great creators of art. The rich kids from happy families were just hangers-on and peripheral to the scene. River had a difficult relationship with his family, but in a sense he didn't fit in. He was like a Michelangelo character in the nineties Renaissance scene. This and his relationship with his dad was what was driving the self-destructive behaviour. I loved him for his talent and I loved him for his activism, but I knew I shouldn't get too close. I needed someone more stable. Samantha had to deal with River now.

'The band were good that night, as I remember it, and I had a tonne of great photos of the show, as well as some of the mingling moments before and after. During the performance, everything seemed fine. There wasn't enough room on stage, so River remained in his booth with a guitar. It was then that people believe Frusciante gave him the heroin, but no one knows for sure. I personally didn't see anything unusual going on and I was friends with John too. Late into the band's set, around the time they played a song called 'Michael Stipe', we heard Samantha screaming outside. There was a lot of commotion. River was in convulsions on the floor. Joaquin was calling for help. Rain was trying to give her brother mouth-to-mouth resuscitation. He was turning cyanotic, in full cardiac arrest and in asystole. The paramedics who arrived tried to restart his heart with medication. I believe it was actually Samantha and Flea that ended up going with him to Cedars-Sinai Hospital. He was pronounced dead at 1:51am on the morning of Halloween. We remember it every year by celebrating Halloween to the fullest and with the most excessive rituals. It is our little tribute to our dead love. Johnny Depp continued to close the club that day every year though, in tribute to his dead friend. I am not sure what River would have thought of that.

'They say Frusciante hid himself away for weeks afterwards in paranoid fear of having a reputation as the pusher. He was suicidal for a while and, to add to it, River's father got involved, threatening to kill him anyway. In the end though, no charges were ever pressed and people calmed down and moved on.

'The following day the whole area was like a shrine. Fans and mourners intermingled with flowers, candles and graffiti messages on the walls of the club. I have a lot of photos of that which I have never sold to any publications. He was the vegan James Dean. I still love him.'

I had to get away from Candy now. Her telling of the story to her friend in the Leftfield tent, within earshot of our oldest son, had upset me and I needed to go for a walk.

It was Saturday evening and Bruce Springsteen and the E Street Band were headlining that night. I had always been a fan, but my wife never was. I had watched Blur headline the night before and was excited for Neil Young's closing slot on the Pyramid Stage on the Sunday night too. I wanted to get away from my family for a few hours and experience these moments alone and amongst a crowd of strangers.

I wandered over to the Pyramid Stage. It was still daylight and there was a crackling excitement in the air. The E Street band were about to walk on stage and I gradually pushed my way closer and closer to the front. As I was doing this, I felt my mobile phone buzzing relentlessly in my pocket. I took one look. It was Candy. I didn't answer. I wanted to be alone in the crowd right now.

Bruce came out onto the stage with an acoustic guitar and a harmonica and the crowd erupted.

I was from a happy, stable family. My parents were still together. They had never taken hard drugs. My siblings led sober and sensible lives. I had never lost anyone major in my life or had parents criticise my path or life choices. Was this why Candy had chosen me over all the hell raisers on the scene? Had she loved River more than me? The guy who was my best friend all the way through high school and college. I knew that I could never ask her that question, but my insecurities were running wild again.

'*I was crawling through a festival way out west. I was thinking about love and the acid test.*'

I followed the widescreen technicolour lyrics and what Bruce sang about in those three minutes were integral to my life and how I would cope with the future and all its predictability and monotony.

The toughest thing is facing yourself. Being honest with yourself. That's much tougher than beating someone up or taking heroin. That's what I call tough.

'*And the rain came in from the wild blue yonder.*'

Gradually, I realised that everything was going to be fine and that my panic attack would pass.

'*As the nineteenth hour was falling up on Desolation Row.*'

I sensed that very few people in the audience knew the song or the relevance and gravity of the moment. No one would have predicted that he would have opened his set this way, with a Joe Strummer song. This was a festival crowd, not his typical audience, so I felt like I understood the risk that he was taking in front of all these middle-class Brits. It was the kind of moment that made you want to go out and get a tattoo.

As the last note of the song ended on Bruce's harmonica, I took my phone out of my pocket again and decided to call my wife back. I wanted to be with her and our son again to watch the rest of the set. We had shared so much already and Joe Strummer said that this next second – clicking his finger – was the greatest thing, because this second has never been lived by anyone anywhere in the world before, ever. Isn't that exciting?

Candy answered the phone calmly and I started walking back through the crowd confidently. Everyone needs a bit of Republican in them to get through this mad and messed-up life, even if we keep it to ourselves most of the time.

UNION SQUARE BLUES (PART ONE)

'Nothing can happen more beautiful than death.'
Walt Whitman

I feel like I need to get this one off my chest. When ideas become too complicated, and the pursuit of perfection is misconstrued as a need for excess; when there are so many people around you that individual personalities can't be discerned; when it is almost impossible to break the rules of excess, then a new set of rules take over. Beauty needs to be found in simplicity, in the discovery of apple blossom or in the loneliness of a park bench with no inscription on it. Yet we can only become simple to a point and then there is nowhere else in this world to go. However, even if the desire to achieve happiness through simplicity is less exciting (when you are sitting on a park bench in Manhattan), my mind needs to see the simplicities that matter in life in order to put them together into something more complicated that could enable me to feel alive again.

I have been tripping a lot lately. It has a fleeting ability to ease my pain, but I am becoming numb to it. Yesterday, I was sitting on the sidewalk on Union Square, surrounded by people whose best friends were in their heads, when

I realised that the buildings around me had grown faces and were having conversations with each other. Initially it seemed like great fun and I laughed to myself – their dialogue was smooth and it had energy, yet they were unaware that I was listening. The Wholefoods store was talking to the Bank of America about the way things have changed over the years – first there were cars, then yellow taxis and now the Uber revolution. It was, George Washington on his horse remarked, as if people no longer wanted a challenge; they wanted everything instantly and without effort. How often, the Bank of America interjected, do you see someone feel the excitement of a taxi skilfully hailed these days, like in the days when Woody Allen was making movies here?

Everything seemed fine until the Mahatma Gandhi statue spotted that I was eavesdropping. He hated it and immediately the conversation became pious. They all started whispering and I had to strain my ears to make out what was being said. All of a sudden I became paranoid that they were talking about me and spreading lies and rumours. That asshole Raymour & Flanigan seemed to be the main instigator, with his shifty window eyes. He is overpriced and overrated and needs to fill his time by hustling for friendships with the others.

This was the worst part of the trip. I take acid as a means of escapism, but now my realities and inevitabilities were confronting me and charging at me head on. I had to get away, so I ran into the arms of my old friend Barnes & Noble – the one fucker that was sticking up for me through all of this shit. OK, maybe he had an ulterior motive, but I was suckered in. I rushed to the counter, swore to God

I would take a break from hallucinogenics, and ordered a copy of Allen Ginsberg's *Howl*. Gripping, long and surreal, it occupied my imagination and helped me to escape the escape. I am convinced that there is no Devil, just God when he is in a bad mood, and he seems to have been in a right strop with me lately.

My name is Sean, I am forty-two years old and I am badly out of shape. I used to play baseball and have girlfriends, but that was a long time ago now. I live alone and I have never been married. I am a Yankees fan. I have lost touch with most of my old friends because I have no interest in their families or their children. I work as a cleaner now at the WeWork building. It won't last long. I am so broke at times that I can't even pay attention. What do I do with the rest of my time? Well, I trip and I read the Bible. Poles apart, you might think, but only on the surface. Paul shows me the way people should be – which is a great distance from what they really are – and acid shows me how they could be, if they bothered to try. It spices them up and if you've ever taken good acid you'll know what I mean. It makes them fantastical and freakish when actually they are all the same – plain and dull. I can't handle that. Uniformity depresses me. Why dampen one's spirits with reality? A dose of disjointed desire for me every time.

I need an axis, some kind of hold on my life. My Bible is that anchor and a far better one than a wife, a family or a desk job. I am a New Testament man (I hate all the Hell and damnation of the old book and it is riddled with contradictions), but I have to say that the four Gospels don't really do it for me. I mean, four different versions of the same story – how dull! Anyway, one of the writers never even knew Jesus; he just heard stories passed down the grapevine. My real problem with the Gospels, though, is that they deal with the preaching and deeds of someone who was (is) immortal and perfect. Whatever Jesus teaches comes to him with consummate ease, so why should I respect that? I want to hear the advice of someone who is like me, who is very imperfect and has sinned as much as I have (more of that in a minute). So, you see, Paul is my man, his letters to the Romans, Corinthians, Galatians, Ephesians, Philippians, Colossians, Thessalonians, Timothy, Titus and Philemon. I read them a lot when I come down from work and I memorise them too.

Living alone is becoming desperate. Perhaps I should give up. There are only a certain number of times you can read the same words, before you start questioning them and picking holes in them. That was the fate that befell Blind Willie McTell. There are only a certain number of times you can take the same drug before your sanity and will to live disappear. I think I understand now what Mike Patton was singing about in 'Crack Hitler'.

I may give away everything I have and even give up my body to be burnt – but if I have no love, this does me no good.

I have no love. I have no relatives around that I could try to love. I have no friends that match, let alone better, my New York City hallucinations. Maybe I have Paul, but I have no love for him. Our relationship seems strained and distant. To be dogmatic, I have no love lost either. I don't think I cared strongly enough for anything from my past for it to count as love. What is sadder, I wonder, losing someone you love or not having anything to lose? No love lost, I decide.

Wanda, who is another cleaner at the WeWork building, has invited me round for drinks with her family on Christmas Day. She can see that I am alone. I should probably go and make some effort to be nice to her family. She likes old soul music, Motown stuff like Marvin Gaye, Otis Redding and the Temptations. She even tries to get me dancing with her when there is no one else on the fifth floor. Putting *Cry To Me* by Solomon Burke on her phone. I won't be dancing on Christmas Day, especially not with Wanda. This is as much as my strength can muster to tell you right now. This world, as it is now, will not last much longer.

I am having strange and frantic sleep. I sleep long and I sleep short, but I never wake up satisfied. Oh what nightmares I have been having. It is as if a hypnotist was crucified on my ceiling and, in his dying moments, his powers were let loose into the air above my bed. In my nightmares, my past sins have been coming back to haunt me in the most surreal and grotesque ways.

In one such nightmare, I was in a confined space and feeling increasingly claustrophobic, when, for no explicable reason, I grew a cell-bursting erection. What are you doing down there? Why are you doing this to me now? I am not really in the mood. I rearranged my floor position to accommodate my untimely bulge when someone started speaking.

'Don't you think it's time you met your Maker, Sean?'

I looked around, but could see no one. Funny, I thought, truth doesn't make a noise normally. Perhaps

59

there was someone directly behind me or perhaps I had just taken too much acid. I could not fathom a response and so I switched off. Two silent minutes passed and the voice came again.

'Don't you want your day of judgement? It can be today if you want, Sean.'

'Who is that speaking?' I cried out.

'Hello, operator. Look down, just look down, Sean.'

And so I did and was reminded of my erection again. I unbuttoned my jeans and all notions of sanity left me.

'Hello there,' spoke my penis, which was larger than normal and had grown a 'man-on-the-moon' sort of face. 'I am Saint Paul and I have come to bring you judgement.'

'Judgement? What judgement?' I cried out in horror.

'I have come to tell you the answer to the great question, Sean. I am going to tell you whether you are going to Heaven or Hell. You want to know, don't you? I mean I think everyone does—'

'But why you, Paul, and why are you in my penis?'

'Why me? Because you trust me, don't you, Sean? You know me well. I know you do. I have been watching the way you pore over my words and ignore the others. Peter and J normally do this, but I asked for this assignment, especially because I knew you would listen to me more than them.'

'But what about my penis?'

'Oh, don't worry about that. It will be in perfect working order again in a few minutes, although I dare say you won't be needing it for a while. Now listen, before I tell you Heaven or Hell, I am going to remind you of a few things, so that my decision will seem justified.'

'What things?'

My paranoia was not eased by Paul's comradely approach. At that moment I would have settled for Hell and an easy life.

'Well, let's start with what happened when you were twenty-three and living in Charlotte, Sean.'

I was alarmed that the voice in my penis had now become female and I sensed that I could recognise it from a long time ago.

'You slept with me in Charlotte and made me a sinner too, Sean. I was married and you knew it, but still you stuck that hideous thing in me. Don't try and pretend it didn't happen, Sean, because we both know it did. A married woman is bound by the law to her husband for as long as she lives.'

I recoiled and tried to get away from my tormentor, but I couldn't, because it was a part of me – actually attached to me. Wherever I put my head or legs, Paul was always close by.

Then the voice in my penis changed again, this time to a soft and effeminate male tone that I instantly recognised.

'Remember me, Sean? When you were living in Los Angeles in your early thirties and feeling lonely, you said you wanted to experiment with a drag queen, and so me and you had some fun. Men do wicked things to each other, Sean, and as a result they bring upon themselves the judgements of all those with narrower minds.'

I woke up in a cold sweat and screaming, before Paul had a chance to tell me anymore. HELL. HELL. HELL. Just let me go to Hell quickly, I can't handle the suspense.

WEDNESDAY:

I can't handle suspense just like I can't handle reality. They are one and the same really. When I am under the influence, I live in a time zone that I can't describe to anyone. All I can feel is potential foreboding and imminent danger. I wrote a death letter, but didn't mail it to anyone.

THURSDAY:

My nerves are on edge now and my pupils are dilating. I need to get away from Union Square and take the PATH train west. I have come to a great decision. Paul is no longer my mentor or wise counsellor. He has been fired. I have thrown the holy books out and created a funeral pyre for them in my head. I do not feel guilty. Anyway, from what he said, he needed me more than I needed him. I can't be so flippant. It masks my fear. Half my world has tumbled down and I am immediately dismissive. Who am I trying to kid? I am a coward, a traitor, a turncoat.

FRIDAY:

I cannot wait for Paul. I cannot wait for Wanda or Christmas. I must act now whilst my impulses are still strong. I am going to end it. I am going to kill myself. But how? How? I am not fond of pain. I don't want to poison or gas myself. I also have no access to a gun. I spend the day tossing the options through my mind. Suicide. Su-i-cide. In the evening I have my brain wave. I live near a railway line and I could lie on it. But I still want to numb the pain. Jack Daniels. I was always fond of Jack Daniels. Two big fuck-off bottles of Jack Daniels and the railway line it is, then. I feel better. I go for a walk.

SATURDAY:

December is the most polished and suave month. The trees look more human than ever and the bushes and hedges are black and wiry. This chill is fresh and we have not tired of it yet. I stride out and I feel invigorated. Perhaps I have been cured. I walk out of the city into New Jersey, through the snow and the slush. Blue collar and close-knit communities. I have never known either. I could live out here and deny my past sins. The voices in my head. Saint Paul coming back and telling me of the rapes. I could lie flat on my back out here at night and sing to myself and no one would care, just another homeless bum who has lost his mind. I could make a new start as a panhandle rambler, like a character in a Joe Ely song. Children would stare at me and mothers would warn them away. In New Jersey, I would be somebody people would notice. That is something that hasn't happened to me for a while.

I watch the sunset in Asbury Park, not long after half 4pm. I cannot stay out here. I must go back. I could go and get my fortune read by Madam Marie. She might talk to me of a promising future or of love.

I must get back. I walk with my head down in sadness and think of a life that I have glimpsed today, but which cannot be mine in the future. It is too late. The boardwalks are for the ambitious and Atlantic City is for the brave.

SUNDAY:

It is Christmas Day now and the whiskey is sitting on the fireplace. I have just returned from an hour with Wanda and her family and I could not handle it. Her family talked only of their lives. No new ground was covered and I became bored quickly. Everyone at her house seemed like a stereotype. I was craving some acid. The first thing I did when I got home was pick up my Bible.

Do you, my friend, pass judgement on others? You have no excuse at all, whoever you are.

There will be a train passing soon and so I start to make the long walk, a bottle of Jack Daniels in both hands. I find my spot. I sit down and I start swigging away. No chattering buildings or talking penises here. No acid. No Wanda. No Paul. No God. Just me, two bottles of whiskey and a train approaching. The night is peaceful and the stars are out. I finish one bottle and I am long gone. None of us lives for himself only; none of us dies for himself only. I have to disagree.

RODRIGO'S LAMENT
(THIS LAND IS NOT YOUR LAND)

In a world of conflict, it is the job of thinking people to be on the side of the oppressed, not on the oppressor.

I claimed that I saw land first and that I deserved the promised reward. However, I was never granted it. Our captain took the spoils and his day is celebrated as a national holiday every year and his story is taught to our children gloriously in schools all over the world.

'Who are those people, Rodrigo?' Columbus asked me.

I did not know as I had never seen their like before. Weeks on end aboard the ship had played devilishly with my senses. I had put on weight and I had slept badly every night. The rocking of the boat on the waves had caused nausea and schizophrenia in some. We had all tired of each other's company and we were all in need of dry land and solitude. No women travelled on the great boat and this meant two things – there was no tenderness to anything new we saw and there were men who let out their passions and desires on each other, because there was no alternative. I do declare that I too indulged myself at night after certain volumes of Spanish wine had been drunk. I boarded the ship with a thirst for adventure and a thirst for new experiences. I was also searching for some form of greatness for future generations to remember me by. I cared little for gold, but legend, I did crave that.

'I don't know, master, but I will go ashore and speak with them.'

I jumped out of the boat and splashed my way through the waist-deep water. With land at my feet, my body felt invigorated for the first time in weeks. My wife back in Europe would surely be proud of me now, because I was doing something no man had ever done before.

Naked and muscular men and women of the Bahama Islands ran towards me, full of excitement and happiness. I knew that I was supposed to guard myself against new people. I remembered the words of the Bible that my shipmates had drilled into me in the preceding weeks, yet I was not scared. I knew instantly that these Arawaks wanted friendship and companionship. I wanted it too, but I knew that my shipmates had no time for these things.

As I walked ashore, carrying my sword, these men and women brought me gifts and food and water. Some of them had parrots and others had balls of cotton. They wanted to share things with me, and we communicated in smiles and grunts and I felt safe at first. However, this soon changed when my shipmates came ashore.

Columbus stood next to me and showed a family his sword, and allowed the mother to cut herself on it out of ignorance. As the blood dripped into the ocean, the family's mood turned to fright and uncertainty.

'Look at these people; their spears are made of cane,' one of my shipmates laughed.

'They would make fine servants,' said another.

The world I had travelled from was obsessed with Renaissance greed. The religion of popes was totalitarian and unforgiving. The governments of kings valued slaves and gold. The frenzy for money was as great then as it is in a Wall Street banker of today. I knew I was the outsider. I was the only person on the ship who valued peace and harmony.

'Come on, Rodrigo. You need to toe the line on this one. Think of your family back home and the riches you can gather for them. A yearly pension of ten thousand maravedís for life!'

I never received the money. I just stared at the blood in the saltwater and wished I had never boarded that ship.

The Arawaks lived in village communities. They had their own agricultural systems of corn, yams and cassava. They could spin and weave and they wore tiny gold ornaments in their ears.

Over the coming days, Columbus took these people onto his ship as prisoners and we sailed to Cuba in search of gold. When we returned, the Arawaks put up a resistance to our cruelty, but they faced Spaniards with armour, muskets and swords. My shipmates now burnt the prisoners to death and hung them. I once saw two of my crew track down two young boys on a beach, each carrying a parrot. They stole the parrots from them, decapitated the boys and then spent the evening drinking rum in celebration. In two years, through murder and mutilation, a quarter of a million native people lay dead.

There was nothing I could do to stop it. After a while, I knew there was no escaping the guilt I was feeling for what we were doing to these poor people. I did not want to return to my wife and family and be taunted by the never-ending shame, but I knew I couldn't stay alive and watch more cruelty in front of my eyes. I took my own life by swallowing cassava poison.

And the quiet acceptance of conquest permeated our history books. And America was born. And thereafter followed all the atrocities and barbarities that led us to where we are now.

MID-COVID-19 LOCKDOWN DEPRESSION BLUES

'No matter how I struggle and strive
I'll never get out of this world alive.'

Hank Williams

The lockdown is tough and my sleep has been seriously affected by it. Working from home every day. Cooking for myself every day. Stuck in total isolation with no certain future. I have been sleeping longer than usual and waking up feeling awful. I am being haunted by voices every night too. She is following me, the Maid of Orléans, shadowing my every step and talking to me in my sleep. There must be a reason she is specifically speaking to me. Is it because I am a Muslim? Is it because I too am a cross-dresser? Why me? There are no opportunities to go out right now, dress up, look attractive or even wear tights. My judgemental community is too preoccupied with the virus and the daily news surrounding it.

By day I am unhealthily attached to my iPhone – Zoom calls, Skype calls, the Houseparty app, WhatsApp messages, the constantly depressing news cycle. I just need some peaceful sleep, but it won't happen. She seems intent on talking to me as I lay terrified and alone in my double bedroom. I don't know if I will be able to enter the world again in a normal state – the voices in my head are playing havoc with my sense of sanity. I am evidently a weak man. I have tried to go to the Quran, I have tried to go to the great philosophers, I have tried to go to the great playwrights, but none of them seem to understand the pain I am in. I decided to stop reading a while back and I tried immersing myself in alcohol and sex instead, but the relief from my torment was only temporary. Maybe I need to sell my body online? It could be the only answer in the lockdown. Instead, I have to hear her every night in my head.

'They called it the Hundred Years' War afterwards, but no one knew what was happening at the time, Eric. The history books have canonised me, but I was just doing what I was doing to boost morale. I died on 30th of May, you know, and that date is coming around soon. I was only nineteen years old. Every year now, Le Pen and her Front National followers gather at my statues on that day. They don't represent me. You are the only person I speak to now, Eric. And I need to speak to you every night.'

Every damn night, I think to myself. And I lie there in bed at 1am and at 2am and at 3am. As if my body was full of caffeine, even though it isn't. I only hear her voice, I never see her. 2am, it is OK, I could still achieve six hours sleep. 3am, now I am starting to go mad. 4am and it will soon be light outside. Why me, Allah, why are you allowing me to be tortured by this nineteen-year-old girl?

'They burnt me at the stake, you know, and I was eventually declared a martyr. Then, hundreds of years later, Napoleon Bonaparte flared up my fame and importance.'

She tells me this every night and I know it by heart. I can see her surrounded by flames and being reduced to ashes. Some nights I even start to feel sorry for my tormentor, for the nineteen-year-old girl who treats my body like a voodoo doll. I start to feel that we have a lot in common and that we are close. I wonder sometimes if I am in love with her. Yet, in my daylight hours, I know that this is all part of her trickery and that I need to banish these thoughts with clinical precision from my brain. Yet, clinical precision is hard for a revisionist and for someone with too much time on their hands during the lockdown.

'We are similar, me and you, Eric. Sometimes I think we are one. I came to prominence at a time when my country was recovering from a great pandemic. The Black Death had ravaged France in a way far more brutal than anything you are seeing now. Henry V had won at Agincourt and many French towns had been captured by the English. You are English, I believe? Can you imagine having that power over me? Like the power that I have over you now. The Dauphin was only fourteen and totally clueless and out of his depth in terms of leadership and military tactics. After Henry V died, his brother John of Lancaster acted as regent, because his son was still a child. By 1429, all of Paris and Rouen was controlled by the English. On the fate of Orléans hung the whole of our kingdom…'

During the daytime I am able to free myself from her voices. Sunlight appears to cleanse my ravaged mind. I walk in the garden and I have my phone calls. We know that the economy will be ruined by this for years to come. Yet I know no one who has actually had the virus. Surely the Black Death was more visible? Is a visible tormentor more bearable than an invisible one, I ask myself. My job is secure and safe, but my sanity is not. Night-time keeps returning and I am alone every night. There is nothing I can do to prevent the darkness. There is nothing I can do to prevent the voices in my head. If I make it through to the other side of this, I will publicly renounce Islam forever. My family in Bury Park may disown me, but I have to find a way of breaking free.

I settle down to sleep once again, but the voice comes at me again as soon as my head hits the pillow.

'I started having visions when I was fourteen. I saw Saint Michael, Saint Catherine and Saint Margaret. These were the visions that told me that I had to be at the king's side. I told Jean De Metz and other people, but no one took me seriously at first. I had to travel as a male soldier to get to the king. This is where the charges of cross-dressing came from that led to my death. This is why you and I are so similar, Eric, and why I feel most comfortable talking to you now.'

In my daylight walks along the nearby roads and tracks, I kept wondering why she was tormenting me. I knew she hated Muslims, but the reasons for this seemed born out of naïvety rather than any understanding of what my religion stood for. I doubted that the Maid had ever read the holy book or had any understanding of the concepts of *hajj* or *zakat* or *jihad*. No, I think it was my Englishness that caused her to pick on me. I felt proud to be a British Muslim and proud that I had grown up in a land that had given birth to Shakespeare and Dickens and all of the great inventions of the Empire. This was instilled in me by my parents. Whilst I was a second-generation

Muslim immigrant, I always enjoyed the duality of the religious traditions that my parents preserved, combined with the best parts of English culture and its idiosyncrasies. The Maid must have detested this about me, because the English of the Hundred Years' War committed so many horrific atrocities against her people. The fight back that she led was like a *jihad* and I knew that many of my family would have admired her for this. Damn it, I respected this nineteen-year-old girl, why did she not just leave me alone now…

'Eric, do you need to sleep?'

'I do now,' I replied. It read 5am on my alarm clock.

'You will never sleep when I am here. I am dressing up in armour for you now and equipping myself for war. A young teenage girl as an effective soldier? I can hear you questioning this. Nothing is believed until it is done for the first time. Like the atom bomb, like the first television set or like Covid-19 shutting down the whole world. And so it turned out that I was able to attend war councils and carry a banner in battle. And so I galvanised my people into a holy war, much like your people are involved in once again.'

If you are the only one to hear voices, you must either be canonised as a saint or a madman. I hunch over my laptop every day at home, sending the e-mails I need to send and trying to communicate as best as I can with the outside world. This communication is all surface, no feeling. I do not communicate that I am going mad, but I write about it to myself in the evenings, to be read posthumously, perhaps. I circle the garden with a mug of coffee in hand each evening, and, as the sun goes down, I debate an internal monologue. Do I let her dominate the conversation and let her own me at night? Or do I fight back and challenge her? If I do this, how will she respond? What will it do to my nights and my ability to get any sleep? What will it do to my days and my ability to disguise my descent into madness? I feel like I am disguising everything well so far, but I live alone and there is no determining if the lockdown will ever end. If I could mix more with people then I could break up these destructive thought patterns. I decide to remain submissive and let her unleash all of her emotion on me. Even I am affected by an era where I have to believe everything a nineteen-year-old girl tries to say to me…

'The French army enjoyed tremendous success during my time with it, and, of course, your country thought I was possessed by the Devil. Do you think I am possessed by the Devil, Eric? I saved the Duke of Alençon's life, and, at the Battle of Patay, the English army was decimated and most of their commanders captured. We claimed Auxerre and Troyes capitulated too, despite the fact that I had been wounded by an arrow, which hit me between my neck and shoulder. People were preaching the end of the world, but I simply drove my countrymen forward to more and more victories. By day, I rallied the troops and inspired the battles and the sieges, but by night I was lonely too, just like you are right now. I knew that this period of my life would not last for much longer.'

They announce on television that the lockdown will be extended. People are terrified of the potential second wave of the virus. There are over thirty thousand dead in this country alone, businesses ruined, sports events cancelled.

All pubs, bars and restaurants will potentially stay closed until Christmas. All I can do is write down my thoughts and allow the Maid to own me and be with me forever. If you truly learn to love your enemies, you became one with them. Your enemies are beautiful, you have to become intertwined with them and harness their strength. I resist fighting the voices in my head and I give myself up to her. I decide to fall totally in love with this girl.

'I am an ardent Catholic, Eric. I hate all forms of other religion. You need to join me.'

'I will,' I respond. 'For you I will do anything.'

'I was captured at Compiègne. Pulled off my horse by an archer. Imprisoned at Beaurevoir Castle and then moved to Rouen and tried for heresy. Then I was subjected to ridiculous levels of hypocrisy. These things still make me angry now.'

'I am sorry for what happened to you and I hope that my words can soothe the pain,' I say to her.

I want her to be happy in my head. I do not want her voice in my head to be an angry voice forever. Maybe it has fallen to me to be the one person that can heal her now?

'Thank you.'

And I sense the anger subsiding and her voice snuggles up next to me in bed.

'I was denied access to a legal advisor. I faced a tribunal stacked with pro-English clergy. I was tried for cross-dressing. Yet I only wore soldier's clothes to deter the English from raping me in prison.'

The Maid sounds sleepy now and I feel her wrapping her arms around my chest from behind. I cannot see her, but I can hear her breathing and I can feel her touch.

'I was eventually declared innocent,' she whispers in my ear.

'I know. And I love you. I love your solitude. And I love your pride.'

I renounced my patriotism and I renounced my previous religious affiliations that night. It was the first night that I could feel her body next to me as well as hearing her voice. Instead of having an angry tormentor, I sensed that I now had a new lover.

Maybe the Maid is at peace now, sleeping next to me. The next morning I work uninterrupted at my desk, looking forward now to the night-time when I will feel her touch again. I decide to abstain from alcohol and caffeine. Madness? What is madness? Isn't life madness? Later that week they announce that the lockdown will be lifted gradually throughout the summer. Gatherings of up to five people may soon be allowed again, they say. I give off a wry smile when I hear this. I don't want this; I am happy now with my duality, I am happy now with my lover. I know that the Maid has short hair and may even resemble a young man, gripping me from behind.

Each night was going to be beautiful now that I loved my enemy. Each day now had purpose and meaning now that my enemy and I were at peace with each other. The world would find a way of returning to normal and I had found some peace in my own company at last.

NO SUPEREGO, ALL ID

You have to make mistakes in life and you have to keep making them without regrets, in order to really feel alive and achieve happiness. This process comes easier to some people to others. It is all about getting the right balance of the ID and the superego.

I desperately don't want to fall in love with anyone. It just causes me pain and heartache. No good can come out of the whole process in the long run. The chance of the person you have fallen in love with also falling in love with you is so slim that the risk isn't worth taking. I have learnt this the hard way many times.

Tonight I can't be bothered with cooking for myself, washing up or watching other people's lives on television, so I decide to go to a busy pub nearby on my own instead. I have a friend who works there. I order a steak and ale pie. It arrives quickly and I enjoy the gravy, the peas and the whole experience. I have a feeling that something new is going to happen tonight and so I sit and observe with the empty plate in front of me. My barman friend now pours me a large brandy – 'He who aspires to be a hero must drink brandy.' Of course, there is a big difference between aspiration and reality. There is also a big difference between what I am like now, relatively eloquent and articulate, and what I will be like when I stumble home tonight.

I have a dangling conversation with my friend about some poetry I read on the Underground walls earlier that week. Words that had puzzled me and I needed to share with someone. Then she walks in. I have had girlfriends who were Polish, Indian, Greek and Persian. But I had never seen anyone like her before. I feel addicted from her first movements and a glance in my direction. Long black hair, dark skin, tall and dominant, she sits down with a group of other girls her age. She looks around twenty-three years old. Andy Warhol would have loved to paint her. Lenny Bruce would have built up a whole new repertoire for her. I look into my glass of brandy. I hope I don't fall in love with her.

Her friends are good-looking too, but they don't interest me. If you asked a bunch of guys younger and less broken than me, they would not pick her out. Her friends are the peacocks, the eye candy, but I sense straight away that she is the slow burner. I watch them all interact with each other and I notice that she is totally spontaneous and unaffected by all around her. She seems to say and do what she feels – all ID, no superego – yet her movements and words don't embarrass her. She just looks natural and right. Right for me.

I become aware that I am staring at this group of girls too much and I feel self-conscious. I turn back to my barman friend and order another brandy. Forest played well last night. Could get into the play-offs at this rate. A lot will hinge on the big Millwall game next Saturday however. We need to learn to preserve a lead and to retain better possession in midfield. We disagree on our best teams and the conversation veers back to the Brian Clough era and the *I Believe in Miracles* movie. He had them train by running through stinging nettles and eating chip butties by Trent Bridge. This conversational slumming is a well-trodden path for me. I order another brandy in an attempt to break out of the rut. I need the Dutch courage. I need it to help me to fall in love with someone new. Being alone is fine if you want it, not if you don't.

She is having a good time and I can't take my eyes off her. I am not usually like this, you know. I am usually too wrapped up in my own world. She looks like my kind of person – unpretentious, uninhibited and looking for a good time, but also intelligent and capable of great intimacy. I never seem to meet anybody like her these days. Oh, I hope I don't fall in love with her.

Two guys arrive at their table and start talking to the girls and I immediately feel pangs of jealousy. Have I missed my chance? Perhaps I need a wingman. Should I have approached her earlier? It was probably a lot easier for these guys. They appeared to have a connection – through university or a mutual friend or something. I have no ice-breaker and this daunts me. I have to create my own luck and the thought leaves me weary.

I can take rejection, a simple 'I'm not interested', and I also don't mind making a fool out of myself, because, well, what have I got to lose? She will either think I am alright, in which case she will keep talking, or she will think I am a nuisance, which I will detect quickly and so I will walk off and never see her again. Nothing ventured, nothing gained. It is always good to analyse the options at an early stage. Yeah that is right…but I just need a good first line and I can't think of one at the moment. I also need those other two guys to piss off. I wish I could just zap them and make them disappear, but for the moment I will use them as an excuse for stalling. And I will continue to pretend that my life is on the mend. I need something to give me my mojo though. I'll have another drink. Courage. Dutch courage.

The pain-in-the-ass guys have honed in now on two of her friends – the eye candy ones. Sometimes life is so predictable. Maybe if I was predictable my life would be simpler and I wouldn't have all this hurt inside me. I would be settled down with a nice girl that my parents approved of and I would be paying off the mortgage and changing nappies. Hmmmm. I have never really wanted that. I would like to stay a complicated fuck-up just for a little while longer. I hope, for her sake, she doesn't fall in love with me.

She is looking lonesome now as her friends are being chatted up. I can see how she resembles me more and more. Loneliness is the river of the world. She fidgets and tries to find things to do. No one is talking to her. I become aware for the first time that she has noticed me. We make eye contact for what seems like a long time, but is probably only five seconds and it ends up being me who looks away. Jeez, maybe she will end up seducing me. Funny how the people you put on a pedestal often turn out to be so vulnerable. I should approach her now if I have any guts at all. She is looking at me again and my pathway is clear. My peripheral vision is blurry and I feel her beckoning me. It feels like the scene in the dance in *West Side Story*, when Tony and Maria walk towards each other and dance for the first time. There are no rival gangs or racial issues to overcome here, though. In fact it should be so much easier – the only thing that needs to be overcome is my inertia. I stand up and take a step forward and she sees this, but then something stops me. I think of how I look being on my own and how I am going to explain this to her. I am waiting for someone? I have been stood up? I am a lonely old divorcee on my own? No. None of these sound convincing. I hover for a while and someone takes my seat at the bar. All the world is green and complicit! Fate is pushing me into the act. Hell, she looks good and I can really be a witty and entertaining guy when I am on form. Right – see that frown on her face, I am going to break it forever. I am going to put the spark back into her life. I am the man she has been waiting for. Seize the day. Seize the day. Don't let opportunities like this pass you by. It might be a lifetime until another girl like this comes along. I want to grow old without regretting tonight. I take two steps forward, feeling confident, but I am foiled. She turns to a friend and starts laughing at a joke. I am frozen by her cold laughter. I go to the toilet.

Nearly. Nearly. I almost seized the day. I just need to choose my moment more carefully. I am going to go back to the bar and get one more drink, just so that I've got something in my hand for when she is talking, and stand closer to her group, so that I can detect when the vital moment will be. Oh yes, I feel good now and I am enjoying this – the strategy, the plotting, the hunt. Come on. Let's have it. The chase is better than the catch, as Lemmy once sang.

'Double brandy please, Jimmy…Oh, and a gin and slimline tonic as well.' I am going to take the bold approach.

I grab the two drinks and swirl around enthusiastically. She has gone. They have all moved on. My eyes search the pub and then I go to the window and look out, but all I can see is groups of men talking to each other. She has flown off into the darkness. I go back to the bar. There is going to be a lock-in and my friend invites me to stay. He thrusts another brandy into my hand. I look at it without commitment. I feel as dead as Boris the Spider. All the good in the world you can put inside a brandy glass, and still have room for you and me. I think I just fell in love with her.

THE BOY IN THE BUBBLE (PART THREE)

I am still a teenager and my stutter has been getting worse than ever. All my life people have made fun out of the way I talk. Boys sarcastically copy me and sometimes degrade me for the colour of my skin too. Girls just generally avoid me because they think I am weird. Being black, in a mainly white neighbourhood, having this speech impediment and having a constant internal crisis of confidence has meant that my only solace has been in my lucid dreams. These dreams make me proud. I am able to float into other worlds and into other conversations and time-travel too.

Recently I have been having conversations with three black musicians that had always fascinated me with their charisma, talent and contradictions. Let me take you into the world of the narcoleptic obsessive that I am. The shiny house of my dreams is full once again. It is wintertime outside and I turn the key in the old oak door. I hang up my coat and hat and I can hear the voices in the kitchen talking loudly and with extreme confidence. I stand in the doorway, as the main tenant of the house, and I feel the love all around me.

'Elliott, you are back! Praise the Lord!'

'How are you, R-R-R-Robert?'

'I have been singing a lot more blues songs today, but I have had to keep those other two madmen out of your kitchen. You know my ancestry is steeped in slavery and so the blues is all we got sometimes. I used to sit in Robinsonville, Mississippi, and just play and play. You know, I only ever wrote twenty-nine songs though, most of which are about pain. You know about pain, don't you, Elliott? Like when they are mocking you.'

'I d-d-d-do know it well.'

'So you gotta channel that pain into artistic expression. Like when my sixteen-year-old wife and our baby died. The only way I could deal with it was to write a song. No good art ever comes out of happiness.'

I knew this fact well and it was why I had all these lonely and crazy people in my house when I dreamt. Their sadness and loneliness made me feel safe. I never knew anyone like these people in my waking life.

'Let me tell you about women, Elliott – I had one in every town as I hitched my way around Mississippi. I remember walking to that crossroads where Highways 61 and 49 met and I made my Faustian pact right there and then. I sold my soul in order to have the best guitar-playing skills. But the Devil caught up with me soon after. I seduced the owner's wife at a juke joint residency one night in Greenwood. I then let my guard down and drank some whiskey from an open bottle that a stranger thrust in front of me. Sonny told me he thought it was poisoned with strychnine...'

Robert's monologue came to an abrupt end when another man, who looked like an older version of me, came crashing down the stairs with his own guitar in his hand.

'You never did sell the amount of records I did. You never did sell music to white kids in your lifetime the way I did. I was so popular that even the Beach Boys wrote a song that was note for note mine. Note for damn note and I never got a penny for it!'

'D-d-d-did you write anything t-t-t-today?' I asked.

'Goddamn, I could not concentrate today with that big old queen upstairs shouting and hollering and your other friend here playing all his depressing songs in the kitchen.'

'"Love in Vain" – who wants to know about love in vain when you can have Maybelline? Now look, Elliott – my daddy was a deacon and my mother was a schoolteacher and they both taught me you gotta look for the fun in bad situations. You gotta live the bad situations and then convert it, like an alchemist, into fun times. I spent time in jail for armed robbery you know, but that tough time always spurred me on.'

I was glad I lived in a world after Martin Luther King and the civil rights movement. I found life tough enough as it was, but before the sixties it must have been a living hell.

'You know what, I had to deal with real bad racism in the early days. Segregated audiences, getting thrown out of diners with Leonard in the south because of the colour of my skin. Even having to give large amounts of my royalties from hit records to white DJs like Alan fucking Freed for playing my music on the radio. Could you imagine that type of thing happening now? Racism is more subliminal for the most part in America these days, but then you see what they just did to my brother George

Floyd in Minneapolis last week and it all comes rushing back to the surface.'

I could sense the tension between the characters in my house and knew that they hadn't been getting along well before I arrived.

'C-c-c-can I get you a d-d-d-drink?' I asked my exuberant friend as we moved towards the bottom of the stairway.

'No, man, that means we gotta go into the kitchen and hear that young twenty-seven-year-old boy moaning about all the bad stuff he has gone through. It frustrates me. I have been through much worse and yet I channel it, you understand, I channel it. Everything I write about isn't about me; it's about the people listening. This is why I sell more records than anyone else in this house.'

We exchanged wicked smiles at this point. His braggadocio was too infectious at times and he punctuated his roaring soliloquys with moments of humour and tenderness.

'Of course, I would have been even bigger if I hadn't been busted for violating the Mann Act when I was at the peak of my fame.'

'W-w-w-what is the M-M-M-Mann Act?'

'Elliott, do you not know anything about me? Shoot – I got done for transporting a woman across state lines for immoral purposes. I served my second period in jail, twenty months this time, and it hurt my career bad. Just because Janice Escalanti, a Native American girl from Yuma, Arizona, told the police that she wanted to go home. I could have been way bigger if I was white like Elvis. He drove young girls across state lines all the time and nobody cared at all—'

At this point, a lot of hollering and noise was made upstairs and the big queen himself appeared at the top of the stairway.

'You complaining again about the colour of your skin?'

'Well, I'll be damned if it isn't the star of *The Girl Can't Help It* himself!'

'It wasn't the colour of your skin, sweetie-pie, it was the fact that you always wanted to sleep with white women. You needed to be more like me!'

'More like you? I can't even play the piano. Even Elliott knows that. Even that miserable boy in the kitchen knows that too.'

'I grew up in Macon, Georgia, and I learnt fast that if I wore make-up and talked all effeminate, then the white girls would love me and come to my concerts. The white boys were not jealous, because they knew I was gay. And I will admit that your guitar playing can, sometimes, make my big toe shoot right up in my foot! But you are always gonna anger the white man by flirting with his women, even filming them in the toilets of your rest-er-rants!'

'Hell, you big old queen, now you got me real mad. You trying to tell me who I should and shouldn't sleep with?'

'I am saying I know a whole lotta things you don't. I became mesmerised by Evangelists as a young boy and the great performers who passed through town in the travelling medicine shows, and I joined Sugarfoot Sam's minstrel show as a dancer.'

'Well, hell!' screamed the older guitarist stood next to me. 'I am gonna run up them stairs and make sure you catch Hell.'

'Come on up, then.'

The debate had become really fiery now and there were egos clashing, but I also knew there was mutual admiration and love under the surface that meant these champions were all safe in each other's company.

The old queen had been through hardship too, much harder than mine. His father had been murdered and he worked for a long time washing dishes at a local Greyhound bus station in New Orleans to make ends meet. It was from there that he found a way of 'channelling his grief' by putting his hair into a high pompadour style and wearing dense eyeliner, face powder and flamboyant on-stage outfits.

'Come on upstairs, why don't you both, and I will play you some boogie-woogie piano. I want to pump my piano, beat them keys you hear me.'

At this point, the two musicians downstairs both raced up the stairs and music started to appear in a far-off place above me.

That was enough entertainment for me for the night and I turned back to the front door, put on my coat and walked out onto the dark street again, leaving my bubble, and knowing I would soon have to face the cold real world again and all its injustice and torment.

As I walked a few blocks and looked up at the full moon, I thought of the influence that the three African American men in my house that night had had on the world. From Led Zeppelin and Fleetwood Mac, from the Beatles and the Rolling Stones, right through to Prince's hairstyle and mannerisms in 'Purple Rain' and 'Under the Cherry Moon', and Elton John's flamboyant style at the piano stool and every other androgynous make-up-wearing rock star in history. Thank God for the outsiders and thank God for the misfits, who had done time in jail and suffered the death of their loved ones at an early age. Without them life really would not be worth living.

BRUCE SPRINGSTEEN'S
NEBRASKA ON VINYL

You get a feeling for a person when they walk into your record shop. Firstly, you study how they are dressed and what giveaway signs that entails. Do they have a punk-rock haircut? Have they got any mod leanings? What age were they first likely to go to gigs?

I can tell the Ramones fans from the Jam fans, and the Clash fans from the Stranglers fans by their clothes and by their haircuts.

Then you want to observe which part of my store they gravitate to first. Everyone goes for comfort initially in a record shop; experimentation only happens after the first ten minutes. I sell all sorts in here and have extensive sections of the shop dedicated to rock and roll, folk, blues, reggae, prog, country, Americana, metal, thrash, punk, soul, rockabilly, mod, ska and gospel. I don't really sell jazz though; it's not for me.

After that you can watch how they interact with other customers and how they might observe social distancing etiquette. The ones who smile more openly at other customers – try to sell them some reggae. The angry ones – get them focused on hardcore punk, metal or thrash.

The best part of my day is when I close up in the evening and decide how to decorate the shop window for the next day. This will have a big impact on who enters or not. Yesterday evening I went with a Johnny Cash twenty-album Columbia box set, the Velvet Underground and Nico, Fairport Convention at the BBC and *The Psychedelic Sounds of the 13th Floor Elevators*. These were the ones I varied – mixed in with all the usual suspects – *Led Zeppelin III*, Sticky Fingers original vinyl with a zip, some Trojan records box sets and a few of the Beatles albums that have the best cover sleeves – I always liked *Beatles for Sale* in that regard, with George Harrison's haircut looking like a pumpkin.

It is true that a man carrying vinyl around town is always accorded a certain amount of respect. Sometimes in my eyes, I stand and look on in awe. I imagine myself walking around the Mekong Delta or through the bustling Khao San Road in Bangkok with a copy of Bob Dylan's *Highway 61 Revisited* under my arm.

You should come on down to the shop one day and find out for yourself about the magic atmosphere inside. To start off with, you can browse for as long as you like. I will always have something edgy and interesting playing in the background that might spark your interest in a new artist or a new genre that could lead to days, weeks or years of future enjoyment. I heard Tom Waits's *Rain Dogs* for the first time in a record shop and it sent me off on a voyage of discovery that has changed my personality forever.

Once you have left the shop with some vinyl, you can tackle the world and all its sinfulness with confidence. Prostitutes and hustlers will afford you respect, children will stare at you in reverence and stay quiet for longer periods of time in your presence.

There are men who have been coming to my shop for years and see it as a sanctuary of comfort in an ever-changing and frightening world. Regardless of which awful Conservative prime minister we have, regardless of who is in the White House, regardless of which hashtag is trending the most on social media at the time, regardless of how your football team is doing in an unrecognisable money-obsessed modern era, Bert Jansch's *Nicola* will still sound as great as when you first heard it. The front cover of Queen's *Sheer Heart Attack* will still stir up magical memories of your childhood.

I don't make much money in this industry; I just about stay afloat. But I do it because it's a labour of love. And I am competitive. I want to have the best shop of its type in the country, better than anything on Berwick Street in London or Oldham Street in Manchester. Inside my shop you can find treasures that no one else knows about – rare, deleted Buzzcocks singles, some of Woody Guthrie's recordings that were never intended to see the light of day.

The satisfaction I get from owning this shop more than compensates for my lack of a girlfriend or my lack of material possessions. My absolute faith in the power of vinyl was rewarded this year when, during all the depression and uncertainty of the Covid-19 lockdown period, my shop was able to open again on the first Monday in June and a new customer walked in. He looked like he was in his mid-forties and had leathery tanned skin and wavy black hair. He was wearing a white T-shirt and a stars-and-stripes bandana around his neck.

He told me he had just moved to my area because of the reputation of my shop. He had recently been in the army and fought in Afghanistan, he told me. During one of the fiercest periods of the war, he saw friends and colleagues incinerated around him and he made a promise to himself to seek out peaceful times and spend his quieter later years immersing himself in vinyl records.

'I used to be homeless as a teenager. My mum had died and my dad was in prison for life. I had drug problems and mixed with a toxic crowd. Eventually I got my life together and joined the army in my twenties. It gave me the structure and purpose I needed and the camaraderie too. I did over twenty years of service, all over the world, and now I've decided to move to a quieter part of the world and write about my experiences, whilst taking some basic work where I can.'

I told him I had lived here all my life and started this shop about twenty-five years ago. I also told him I was taking on another part-time member of staff next month and he seemed interested in this. He had an honest look about him and I could tell we would click with each other. Our music tastes meshed and he had a natural charm and roguish charisma to him.

After we exchanged our condensed life stories, he bought a copy of *Nebraska* by Bruce Springsteen and walked out onto the summer pavement with a peaceful life ahead of him. The opportunity for healing time was real for him now. He had emerged from life's horrors, wounded but alive, and with my help had many new worlds to discover.

GUILT

A man lies in his bed at night, consumed by guilt of an unspoken atrocity. He is tired constantly, but he cannot sleep. He turns from side to side in terror, gripping his pillow for comradeship, as sleep dangles itself in front of him like a pendulum created by Edgar Allan Poe. Some light is always creeping through the gaps in the curtains, even at two in the morning – there is something there that won't go away. He gets up, washes his face in the sink and stares at himself in the mirror and talks to himself. He takes his mobile phone off charge and checks the time. He browses on YouTube. He browses on Pornhub. He is looking for the formula, the never-ending secret formula of life and happiness that he cannot find. A tormented soul with tinnitus. Imaginary caffeine still running through his veins like a riptide that is invisible from a distance. He puts his phone on the brown wooden table by his bed, knowing now that the 24% battery will drain from black to red as he tries harder and harder to sleep. At 4am, he goes to the kitchen and makes a sandwich, like the ones Jayda used to make him before the accident. A toasted sandwich. He burns his finger slightly on the silver metallic toaster and he knows now that sleep has run away into the sand dunes; the morning panic is near now and consumes his brain as the sandwich hangs in his mouth, suspended from its fate by memories and fearful ideas. After the milkman delivers his spiritual advice, he decides to walk out onto the road. A dead man walking – he knows that redemption is only possible if he takes full responsibility for what he did. He returns to his bed, takes a sleeping pill and puts two blue foam earplugs deep into his ears. He still cannot sleep and the alarm on his phone goes off at 7:25am. He lies there in agony, waiting for the repeat alarm. Unusually, it never comes and a long time passes. At 8am, he loads up his gun and goes to the study where he has written great works published and great works as yet unpublished. He points the gun under his chin and blows his brains onto the newly painted white ceiling. *Splash.* And still he is unable to sleep. Guilt held firm and moved on to the next man – it is a very tenacious and dogged beast.

A PICTURE OF HER, HOLDING A PICTURE OF ME, IN THE POCKET OF MY BLUE JEANS

'At first flash of Eden, we race down to the sea.'

Jim Morrison

Just like Bobby McGee, I grew a beard, smoked countless cigarettes and hitch-hiked my way through Louisiana and on into Texas. With the quieter drivers, I wrote poetry and short stories and admired the automobiles, the widescreen landscapes and the birds of America. I sometimes jumped on Greyhounds too, and drew inspiration from short and insightful encounters. On the bus from Austin to Phoenix, I met a girl who was running away from an alcoholic and abusive husband. She opened up to me for hours as the other passengers around us were sleeping. It felt like no one else was hearing her story and no one else was caring.

'I married him to keep my family happy.'

I understood, as I had seen plenty of this in my own community.

'Like Kacey Musgraves sang, if you ain't got two kids by the time you are twenty-one, society thinks you are going to die alone.'

Even now, after all the feminism and progression of fifty years. it seemed that women in the southern states of America were still damned if they did and damned if they didn't. And abusive and controlling husbands seemed to still be everywhere.

She talked her head onto my shoulder, and, as we meandered our way through the Arizona desert, two middle-aged, shaggy-haired souls wearing denim snuggled up and kissed for the first time on the Greyhound bus.

As we pulled into Phoenix, she told me of her plans to stay with her sister and sing some backing vocals for a bluegrass band that an old school friend of hers was in. They played at the Rusty Spur every Thursday night – the kind of venue where people knew their Guy Clark and their Townes Van Zandt albums and lived the type of life depicted in the movie *Heartworn Highways*. She got off the bus and gave me her phone number and her sister's address. We took a couple of fun photos on our phones before she disappeared into the sweltering night.

I rode on to San Diego, eager to see the Pacific Ocean, drink in the Gaslamp Quarter and hang out with some surfer friends in Ocean Beach. I did not surf myself, but would be happy to see the Grateful Dead tribute band that played every Monday night and mooch about in Cow Records, purchasing some of the great sixties and seventies California albums – Love's *Forever Changes*, *Strange Days* by the Doors.

A few weeks passed and I thought of the girl on the bus and going back to see her in Arizona. I printed off a couple of the photos we took in Phoenix and kept a picture of her, holding a picture of me, in the pocket of my blue jeans.

Days blended into one in Ocean Beach and my urgency for life had escaped me temporarily, it seemed. A couple of my friends disappeared for a while to the Mojave Desert and this jolted me into some action. I messaged the girl on the bus and sent her a few photos of myself on the beach at sunset.

'How are you? I enjoyed our bus ride together. Did you get a chance to heal yet?'

But I never got a response.

The two tick symbols on my WhatsApp message never turned blue and I guess she never read them. A few days later, I tried calling the number twice, but no one picked up.

Maybe we belonged together, I thought to myself for a few days. Maybe I should have got off the bus in Phoenix and stayed there with her. Maybe the southern California lifestyle isn't for me long-term. Maybe she got back with her husband and never thought about me again…

IT IS NOT DYING, IT IS NOT DYING

'I keep picturing all these little kids playing some game in this big field of rye and all. Thousands of little kids, and nobody's around – nobody big, I mean – except me. And I'm standing on the edge of some crazy cliff. What I have to do, I have to catch everybody if they start to go over the cliff – I mean if they are running and they don't look where they're going I have to come out from somewhere and catch them. That's all I do all day. I'd just be the catcher in the rye and all.'

J. D. Salinger

I am too vulnerable for a world full of pain and lies. So I decided that I wanted to write Chapter 27, so that Holden Caulfield's spirit and hatred of phoniness in this world lived on. Locked in my jail cell, I decided, I would probably stick to the truth. I would confess everything without pause or emotion and a new chapter of the world would begin. Yes, I did kill John Lennon, and although a part of me is Holden Caulfield, a part of me must be the Devil too. My pastor in Decatur, Georgia, was right: there was indeed a demonic power at work. The real hero is usually a hero by accident – he dreams of being an honest coward like everybody else.

I was born in Fort Worth, Texas, in 1955 and the events that led me to the Dakota Building in New York City on 8th December 1980 are easily told. I had a simple childhood, but my father used to fly into rages often and beat my mother. He never beat me, but he never showed any love to me either. This lack of warmth led me into creating imaginary worlds in my bedroom, and these imaginary worlds gave me great power and authority. As I went through my teenage years and into my twenties, I felt this great power grow and grow inside me as if I was the catcher in the rye.

I worked for World Vision for a while, both in the United States and also in Lebanon. A highlight of that time for me was that I once got to meet President Gerald Ford and shake his hand. I cared a lot about children and I wanted to make a difference in their lives. I wanted them to have all the basic human rights that were sometimes denied of them. I also wanted to spread Jesus' word. My relationship with Jesus has always been the most important relationship in my life. I wanted to honour him and spread his message at all times.

I was a Beatles fan for a long time. The *Rubber Soul* album was my favourite – just great short and snappy pop songs and no filler at all. I use to play it over and over again at my parents' house. I loved 'The Word'; it seemed to have spiritual resonance for my lost generation. I also loved 'You Won't See Me' – I sang that song to the imaginary people in my room, who were controlled by me, but to whom I had an invisible godlike power over.

In the seventies I became a born-again Presbyterian and I took up painting and listening to Todd Rundgren albums – *Something/Anything?* and *Hermit of Mink Hollow* were my favourites and still are. I started turning against the

Beatles when I read more interviews and books about John Lennon. He said that the Beatles were bigger than Jesus and that made me really angry. Who the hell did he think he was, saying that? He had no right to belittle my Lord and particularly in such a public way. I realised that so many people followed this guy's advice and lifestyle and I became enraged by it. Some of his solo songs were far worse: in 'God' he seemed to denounce the existence of God entirely and in 'Imagine' he was preaching a form of communism that the hippies were all obsessed with. I was from Fort Worth, Texas, and this sort of communism did not sit well with me, particularly when the writer himself was a multi-millionaire, owning luxury houses and apartments.

My anger consumed me for a while, and I broke up with a girlfriend I had at the time and quit the job I was doing as a security guard in Hawaii. I felt a calling from God at this time, to do something really big to honour him. I attempted suicide by carbon monoxide asphyxiation to begin with, but I couldn't get it right and I realised that God wanted me to stay alive in order to carry out his great work. I went on a seven-week trip around the world with some money I had saved up, in order to search for signs from God and inspiration. I travelled to Tokyo, Seoul, Hong Kong, Singapore, Bangkok, Delhi, Beirut, Geneva, Paris, London and Dublin. My most memorable moment was visiting the Père Lachaise cemetery in Paris one evening and feeling the spirits of all the great dead writers and poets in there – Oscar Wilde, Marcel Proust, Jim Morrison, Paul Éluard, Molière and Balzac. The greatness of their spirits consumed me and made me realise that killing myself would achieve nothing, for I was a nobody and my death would not change the world in any way. I needed to kill someone famous, so that history could be altered. Standing in Père Lachaise was where I first got the inspiration to murder John. Maybe it was Jim Morrison's jealous spirit that jumped into my body. After all, *Abbey Road* sold a lot more copies than *The Soft Parade* and this may have caused intense jealousy in him. In 1968, the Doors had just finished up a European tour and it is rumoured that Jim visited the Beatles in their studio in London whilst they were recording *The White Album* and the song 'Happiness is a Warm Gun'. They say Jim sang backing vocals to the 'Mother Superior jumped the gun' lyric, and that John dedicated the line 'Like a lizard on a window pane' to the Lizard King himself. I don't know the whole story, but it was in Paris where my desire to change the world moved up a gear.

I began a relationship with my travel agent, Gloria, at this time and we married in 1979. I told her many times of my long-term intentions, but she seemed to not really believe me. For a while I thought of killing other people – Liz Taylor, Ronald Reagan, Paul McCartney even. The Lizard King's voice kept telling me to focus on John.

I flew to New York in December 1980. I stayed at a Sheraton hotel and bought tickets to go and see *The Elephant Man* on Broadway, with David Bowie in it. I never ended up seeing the show as my front-row ticket was for 9th December and I had been arrested by then.

On 7th December, I saw James Taylor by the 72nd Street Subway stop. I accosted him and pinned him up against the wall and told him my name and what I was in New York to do that week. I had taken some cocaine earlier on that day and I think he was scared by my manic speech and crazed persona. God was in me, but other forces were in me by this point too. New York was getting really cold and I needed some action to keep me warm. I told Gloria all of this on the phone from my hotel that night. She seemed disinterested and I started wondering if she was having an affair with another man behind my back. Why was she disinterested in my plans and my quest for greatness? It made no sense.

On the morning of 8th December, I left my hotel room and bought a copy of *The Catcher in the Rye*. I signed it, 'To Holden Caulfield. This is my statement, Holden Caulfield.' I walked up the Upper West Side streets along the corner of Central Park from Columbus Circle. The statue of Christopher Columbus appeared to smile and wink at me as I strode confidently northwards – he was, of course, a savage murderer too. The weather was cold, you could see your breath in it and there was a huge sense of anticipation in the air, the type of energy that you would never get in Fort Worth at any time of year. I bought two hot dogs in the late morning from a street vendor and lavished them with mustard and ketchup.

I got to the Dakota Apartments and had on me my copy of *The Catcher in the Rye* and also a vinyl of the *Double Fantasy* album. I spoke to a few other fans milling around and also the doorman, Jose. After a while, I got into a long conversation with a really beautiful girl called Jude. She said that she had been the biggest Beatles fan in her hometown whilst she was growing up. She looked like she was in her mid-twenties now, with long brown hair. Then the housekeeper appeared with Sean and I spontaneously approached them and shook little Sean's hand. 'He is a beautiful boy,' I remarked to myself.

I then asked Jude if she wanted to go for a late lunch with me, before we went back and tried to get John's autograph. She agreed and we walked to a diner just off Amsterdam Avenue, a few blocks away, and I told her all about my previous life in Hawaii. She had never been, she told me, and she seemed genuinely fascinated by my humble life out there. For a while she seemed really into me and it struck me how much more beautiful Jude was than my wife, Gloria. Some of the conversation I had with Jude has always stayed with me.

'So have you listened to the new album yet?'

'Yes, I have,' I replied.

'Well, what do you think of it?'

'It's not as good as *Rubber Soul*,' I responded.

'Duh…well, obviously. But I wasn't expecting that. I just want him to be happy making music again. I think it has some of his best songs on it for some time – "I'm Losing You", "Beautiful Boy (Darling Boy)", "Woman" and "Just Like Starting Over". Don't you think?'

'I think they are OK. Will you go for dinner with me tonight? I think my wife and I are breaking up and I don't want to be alone.'

'Listen mister, you are kind of cute, in a geeky way, but I have only just met you. Two dates in one day is a bit quick for me. Let's go back and see if we can get his autograph together.'

She had rejected me and I walked sombrely by her side on the way back to the Dakota. All this girl seemed to want to do was talk about the music. I think it was all that she had in her life. She obviously didn't have the type of relationship with Jesus that I did and it was like she couldn't be angry at John for anything. She just talked and talked and talked about him reverently as if he was a saint to her or something. This made me more paranoid. Hippy girls like Jude misunderstood him – they were way off from the truth.

At around 5pm, John left the Dakota to get into a limousine and, I guessed, headed to a recording studio. Jude and I both asked for his autograph. Jude asked first and was dizzy with excitement. I then thrust a copy of *Double Fantasy* at him and a BIC pen. The pen didn't work to start with and there was a few seconds of awkwardness. John shook the pen a little and twirled it around his fingers, and, whilst staring at my face, he signed his autograph.

'All systems go now,' he said, just before he put the pen to the vinyl cover. 'Is that all?' he then asked me.

We just stared at each other and I didn't say anything.

'Do you want anything else?'

Again, I kept silent and we held each other's eye contact for a few seconds. It was as if he knew right there and then that he was staring into the eyes of his killer.

I then walked around for a few more hours with Jude talking about Beatles albums, Beatles stories and Beatles scandals. She left me at around nine o'clock, as she had to go and meet some friends in a bar in Greenwich Village and so I walked back to the Dakota and talked some more to the doorman, Jose. Mainly we just kept the conversation to pleasantries, but one thing he did say stuck with me.

'I think John seems really happy these last few months. I have worked here a while and I feel he is at peace with himself.'

Good, I thought. This is how it is meant to be, this is the way Holden would have intended it. This is the way

Jim Morrison's spirit in the Père Lachaise cemetery would have intended it. I walked away and stood leaning against a streetlight and read *The Catcher in the Rye*.

John's limousine appeared again just before eleven o'clock. Yoko got out of the car first and walked ahead towards the doorman and John got out afterwards. He walked past me, he recognised me from before I felt, but he didn't say anything. It was cold, it was dark and it was eerily quiet on the Upper West Side at that moment.

As he walked towards the door of his apartment building, his multi-millionaire, communist, bigger-than-Jesus apartment complex, I assumed a combat position and fired five shots with my Charter Arms .38 special revolver into his back. *Bang. Bang. Bang. Bang. Bang.* I heard Yoko scream and run back towards him. I don't remember much else.

I stayed at the scene, calmly reading my copy of *The Catcher in the Rye*, until the NYPD arrested me. Holden was proud of me. I knew it. We were both anti-phonies and I went on to make the novel my manifesto.

I am talking to you now from the Wende Correctional Facility and I feel good. I have made my peace with Jesus and that is the most important thing for me right now and always has been. I am too vulnerable for a world full of pain and lies. Gloria didn't understand me, Jude coldly rejected me and John had it coming for his arrogance and hypocrisy. This is Chapter 27 and it has no ending. I hope one day to have my parole granted and to continue my great work with World Vision, helping orphaned children in impoverished communities around the world and spreading the beautiful words of Jesus Christ.

PRINCE PROSPERO

'You never know what is enough, unless you know what is more than enough.'

William Blake

I am a walking contradiction. Part fiction, part reality. I can be a lot of fun to be around. I can be an asshole and a morally vacuous shithead too. I survived the masque of the Red Death. The pestilence had been fatal, the pestilence had been hideous. Blood had been the avatar and the seal – the redness, the horror, the sharp pains, the dizziness and the dissolution. Yet I survived it all.

And, many years later, I took Sophie Dee to the races with me. She had never been before and being a Welsh girl, raised in Merthyr Tydfil, she had a passionate and addictive heart and so I wanted to show her the best day out possible.

It was a voluptuous scene, that race meeting at Cheltenham. The sun beat down and sixty thousand people gathered to gamble and drink and shout. I brought a month's salary in lobsters with me, for this was to be no masquerade. This could be the best day ever.

I had read the racing form diligently over the previous weekend and so I knew my strategy. Sophie Dee said she wanted to bet on the horses with the best names and she would draw a lot of attention to herself when she shouted them home. In her late twenties now, Sophie Dee, brunette hair dyed red and a California tan. Although she had spent plenty of time across the Atlantic Ocean, the soft Welsh accent still shone through when it mattered. She had been to plenty of rugby and football matches she told me, but this was a new thing for her. Sophie had dated Ian Watkins, the lead singer of the rock band the Lost Prophets in her teenage years (they were also from Merthyr Tydfil). I didn't really feel like entering into that conversation with her today.

'I want to spend all my winnings in Cardiff, baby.'

We planned to drive back to Cardiff that evening so her idea could easily reach fruition.

'It's nice to do something that gets in the way of the drinking,' I told her as we walked into the racecourse half an hour before the first race.'

'Oh for sure,' Sophie Dee said, 'and this is so much more fun than a day at the zoo! Zoos are stupid! And also, I am glad you are drinking less these days, less than when we first met many years ago anyway. But today…I think I will be a bad influence on you once again, especially if we have some winning bets.'

We passed a few animal rights protesters as we entered the course and then passed the stands selling the *Racing Posts* and the form books. I didn't buy any because I figured I had it all sussed. Then an old gypsy lady tried to distract us and sell us some lucky heather. Sophie Dee wanted to buy some, but I had been tricked into this before and the old gypsy woman knew my eyes as we exchanged looks.

'I have been good to you before. Be good to me,' the old lady shouted at us as we hurried onto the course.

Inside the Tattersalls area of the racecourse, it was densely crowded and you could feel the feverish beating heart of life. Each bookmaker was trying to get the best angles and suck in the mug punters fastest. There were moneyed-up toffs boasting all around me, working-class men with flat caps and an eye for danger, con men and professional gamblers that you would not find on Instagram, some of whom were banned from half of the betting shops in London. The frenetic energy around me was hypnotic. I could stay in this part of the racecourse all day.

Ten minutes to the first race.

'Who are we betting on in the first race, baby?'

'Shishkin,' I replied.

'What are the odds?'

'6/1, baby!'

'Ok, Daddy-O. I want to place the bet.'

And so I gave Sophie Dee two hundred pounds and told her to go and speak to the man by the Starsports sign.

'Just tell him you want to put two hundred pounds on Shishkin.'

'You're all heart, Prospero.'

I was all heart. I was all heart for Sophie Dee on that day for sure. We weren't a couple as such, but we had dated and slept together before and she was as much fun as anyone I knew to go on an adventure with.

We walked up into the grandstand with Sophie Dee clenching her betting slip.

'And they are off, for the two-mile contest.'

And the heaving masses roared out their approval.

Shishkin had yellow colours and was easy to spot in mid division through the first mile, jumping the hurdles smoothly. I felt quietly confident.

'Shouldn't he be nearer the front?' Sophie Dee asked me, as we were pushed up close to each other, surrounded by the racing fanatics and fiends. Damn, she looked good. For the middle section of the race, I just studied her soft features and watched the naïve and pure expressions crossing her face. She responded to the racecourse commentator and the noises of the crowd with intimate facial gestures. Sophie Dee was a damaged person. Her father had abused her as a child. She had run away from home aged sixteen and had a series of not-very-nice boyfriends, including one guy from Merthyr Tydfil who had hit her repeatedly and was now doing time in jail. And then of course there was the whole Ian Watkins saga. Although she exuded so much confidence, I wanted to protect her at times as I felt that she was a magnet for cruel and nasty men. I had noticed also how she had very few female friends and women in general didn't warm to her – they saw her as too much of a trophy girl for men. This reaction was part jealousy and part cattishness, I felt. It was an unfair reaction though and left her extremely vulnerable at times.

The last mile of the race built up to a thrilling climax. The huge crowd started bellowing and roaring as the horses rounded onto the home straight. Shishkin had been placed in fourth, but coming to the final flight of hurdles he moved into second place behind a horse called Abacadabras.

'Come on, Shishkin! Come on, Shishkin!' Sophie shouted.

'We have a chance here, my Calendar Girl.' I gripped her shoulders tightly.

'Oh, this is so exciting! This is the most fun I have had since I went out with Ian when I was a teenager.'

And the horses jumped the last flight of hurdles. And Shishkin and Abacadabras battled neck and neck up the run in together, both horses drawing well away from the third-place horse. The racecourse erupted and so did Sophie Dee as Shishkin passed the post a head in front of Abacadabras.

Sophie Dee and I embraced and kissed each other, and were both pushed around in the melee of excitement as newspapers were thrown into the air. Winning punters all over the course embraced each other. I felt excited and a little bit terrified both at the same time, because I knew now that she could get addicted to this life and this would mean I had to behave better in the future. Like an assembly of phantasms across the betting ring, it may well be supposed than normal life was never going to resume.

'Let's collect our winnings, baby!'

And Sophie Dee marched excitedly down to the Starsports bookmakers pitch with her winning betting ticket and collected £1,400 in fifty-pound notes.

'Do they serve champagne here?'

'Of course they do.'

'Then take me to the bar, baby!'

We went into a crowded bar within the huge racecourse grandstand and passed many paintings of great horses that had won at the course before – Arkle, Night Nurse, Dawn Run, Desert Orchid, Istabraq.

I bought a bottle of champagne with two glasses and we toasted our first race success.

'Who are we betting on in the second race, Prospero?'

'Put The Kettle On,' I told her, 'and this one is 16/1.'

'Oh, that is exciting. Let's put two hundred pounds on it again.'

And Sophie Dee downed three glasses of champagne in about five minutes and I felt compelled to do the same.

We went back to our lucky spot and Sophie Dee placed our bet.

'So this race is a steeplechase,' I explained, 'and the fences are bigger than hurdle races. Because of this, the horses go a little slower, but it can be just as exciting.'

'Why is it called a steeplechase?'

And I bumbled my way through an explanation of the eighteenth-century absurdity of country squires racing from one church to another and across parishes.

'I can't believe I've never done this before. It's brilliant. Ian never took me to the races – it was always gigs and music festivals with him and sitting around getting so bored during band practice sessions.'

I knew I had done it a million times with all kinds of outcomes. The Red Death had nearly killed me, my attraction to women had waned and there were times I had thought of giving up the whole gambling and drinking thing. But somehow today, and with my beginner, I felt more alive and more in love with the voluptuous scene than ever.

I took some photos of Sophie Dee and me with the betting slip in our hands. It read, 'Put The Kettle On, £3,200 win.'

As the second race started, I looked back on my phone at the images and, away from Sophie Dee's stare, I looked deeply at my own spectral image. I stalked myself and I saw myself convulsing, with a strong shudder, either of terror or distaste, and then I felt my brow reddening with rage. I knew what an asshole I could be and how I could run away if I needed to, but I also knew that this time I could stick and see things out.

'Come on, Put The Kettle On!' we both shouted as the horses all passed the grandstand on the first circuit. Put The Kettle On was leading the field from the favourite, Notebook, and a horse called Al Dancer. Notebook was the 5/2 favourite and a number of punters around us clearly wanted him to win.

Once again, as the race unfolded, I turned my attention away from the horses and studied Sophie Dee and her intricate and delicate expressions. She had sass, she was all heart and she exuded the warmth of a friendly madam at a bordello. I knew she could look after me and I knew she could make me a better person. I had had alcohol problems for over a decade, criminal allegations against me and had fallen out with family members and important people in my life. Despite surviving the Red Death, I didn't know how much more of life's madness I could take on my own. My life could go in two directions now, and as some of the seedier racegoers looked up and down Sophie Dee's curves, I just wanted to put my arms around her and hug her tightly. As much as I could save her from the bully-boys of the Welsh valleys, who had beaten her and abused her in the past, she had the power through her positivity and energy to heal my broken body and brain too. If I had the guts to commit to her. I needed to not care about what other people thought and I needed to do this for me and her.

As the horses came down the hill and Put The Kettle On jumped each fence with clarity and purpose, his rivals started to fade away. Notebook, the favourite, started to drop far behind the leaders after the third last fence, to the groans of his Irish supporters around us.

At the second last fence, two horses fell, Cash Back and Esprit Du Large. And as the field of crazed racehorses galloped nearer to us it became clear that Put The Kettle On was striding closer and closer to victory. The crowd was quieter this time because our horse was a long shot and not many people had backed him.

Sophie Dee and I gripped each other tighter and tighter and cheered our horse to an easy victory.

'I love horses!' Sophie Dee screamed out and people around us laughed. She leant closer to me. 'I love them the way I used to love the Lost Prophets!'

Once again she went and collected our winnings. More money now than either of us had had in our hands in a while and we went back to the bar.

This time I ordered two pints of lager and we sat and talked for over an hour and watched the next two races on television screens as we enjoyed our drinks. Sophie Dee told me about her last horrible boyfriend in Los Angeles and his drug addictions and his lies, and told me also of her recent abortion. We had known each other for years, and, although we had sometimes not seen each other for long periods, we always connected instantly and were able to talk about our lives in great depth without fear of judgement or backlash.

'Let's bet on the fifth race, my prince,' she said to me as we ordered two more pints. 'Which horse is going to win? I like the name Honeysuckle. And it's the favourite and it has a female jockey, which I like too.'

'Honeysuckle it is,' I responded, as I fancied this horse too from my form-studying the previous weekend.

We drank up our pints, with the perfect levels of alcoholic electricity running through our bodies, and we calmly pushed our way through the crowds of predators and went back to our favourite spot on the racecourse, between the grandstand and the betting ring. Sophie Dee placed our bet in the usual way.

'Come on, Honeysuckle!'

Why change a winning formula? For a short period of time on that Tuesday afternoon, I knew that my dog days were over. No matter what had gone on before in our lives and no matter what would happen afterwards, I was in love with Sophie Dee and she was in love with me. And the flames that had roared out of the tripods of my past had expired. Darkness and decay were banished, as my life with a Cardiff-born-abused-child-grown-into-porn-star held illimitable dominion over all.

And we held the betting slip together in our intertwined hands.

Honeysuckle. 6/4 favourite. Mares Hurdle. 10th March 2020. What could possibly go wrong in the future?

DEATH OF A CLOWN

The cuckoo bird lays eggs in other birds' nests. It is a habit that cannot be changed or controlled. Fuck you for cheating on me. Fuck you for reducing it to the word 'cheating'. As if this were a card game, and you sneaked a look at my hand. Who came up with the term 'cheating' anyway? A cheater, I imagine. Someone who thought 'liar' was too harsh. Someone who thought 'devastator' was too emotional.

Peter and Janette's bourgeois house in Cheshire had everything a modern couple would need. Sky TV, the best furniture from IKEA, an immaculate garden, an Audi and a Volkswagen Golf parked outside. A big log fire that blazed in the winter. A well-stocked wine cabinet. Peter and Janette were both high-flyers in their respective careers and this was one of the things that appeared to make them such a good match.

Peter, an experienced dentist from a well-connected local family, was exactly the type of man you would want your daughter to marry. Successful in his career, clean cut, healthy and the type of man that elderly women would drool over. He had no enemies, it seemed. Yet had he ever really stood up for anything important or put his neck on the line for a good cause before? He was good at sorting out your teeth and he was good at seeming successful, but he was weak to temptation and always had been.

Janette was a criminal solicitor, a very sharp mind, half Canadian and two years younger than Peter. She was a power dresser and was attracted to success and confidence, but she had more of a backbone than Peter and was definitely the fiery one in the relationship. She was the one who, behind the scenes, made the important decisions and dictated the pace of their relationship and courtship at an early stage. They had married after being together for two years and had two healthy and well-liked children. Many of their neighbours in the village saw them as the perfect couple.

It was a warm Saturday evening in August, and Peter and Janette returned from a dinner with friends in town back to their exquisite house at around 11:30pm.

Peter threw off his jacket onto the living room sofa.

'Did you get enough attention tonight?' he asked Janette.

She looked him directly in the eye with triumph and defiance and then replied, 'I should hope so.'

Peter was feeling confrontational. Tempers had been simmering all evening and were potentially going to boil over. He took a seat facing his wife.

'You made me look ridiculous tonight.'

'Is this an argument?' Janette implored angrily. 'Are you hell-bent on criticising my behaviour?'

'I saw the way that you and Stephen Sanders were flirting this evening. Everyone saw it. It was in front of me and it was in front of everyone. The way you put your arms around him, the sexual references, how do you really expect me to react to that, Janette?'

Stephen Sanders was a previous work colleague of Janette's, and Peter had always felt threatened by him. Of course, it was Stephen who started a lot of last year's problems with that controversial dinner party remark that, 'Statistically speaking, there is a 65% chance that the love of your life is having an affair. Be very suspicious.' Oh, the trouble that that conversation caused later down the line.

'Come on, Peter, don't throw that at me. You have changed your tune since last year. You didn't seem to care before if anyone was paying me attention or not. When I found out last year that you were having an affair – an affair with a woman you were in love with – you knew how much it upset me, yet I have decided to stand by you. You have made me look ridiculous too. You told me that I was perfectly free. Everything you said and did made it clear to me that this other woman of yours was so much more attractive than me. Of course, all of your subliminal messages were perfectly gentlemanly, but fuck you, Peter, you loved her more than me last year! You can't deny that. We agreed to stay together for our kids, if you remember? That was the agreement we made. You said to me all that mattered was keeping up appearances. I could take a lover if I wanted, provided I kept it a secret. Do you not remember the argument in the garden last October? Do you not remember how we left that conversation? I know you do, Peter. You are not that stupid.'

Janette was shouting now and she had complete control over the conversation. Peter wasn't daring to interrupt. His guilt was overwhelming him.

'I understood that you were completely in love with her last year, is that not right? I was a complete nuisance to you. So why are you getting jealous about Stephen tonight? I do not have a lover. I am not a cheating scumbag like you. I have not been unfaithful to you. Yet I could make you a cuckold whenever you want. Deal with that!'

'Janette! This is so over the top. Why are you being like this tonight? The truth is that I'm still in love with you and don't like seeing you flirting with another man. Is that really so hard for you to understand?'

'My dear husband, how you have changed. Look at this house. Look at our children. To the outside world we are the perfect couple. Yet we both know that neither of us has been happy for a long time now.'

'I still fancy you though. Is that allowed?' Peter interrupted.

'Oh, is that right? Well good for you. Give yourself a pat on the back. You must have been fasting lately then, I am guessing. You must have run out of lovers and extra-marital affairs. Am I right?'

'Janette, please, why are you doing this?'

'Why? Why am I doing this? Because all last year when we were sleeping in separate beds and when you were fucking that other woman, I had to suffer in unbearable silence. And watch you spend money on her. Come on, how much did it cost you each month having a lover as well as me? Two grand, three grand extra every month? Goodnight. I don't want to see any more of you. I am going into the other room. Don't even think about trying to come in after me. If I want to take my own lover now, I will. I was upset last year; I was heartbroken by your behaviour. But now I will live my life the way I want to. I don't have to answer to you. We are together for the children, but I am not in love with you anymore.'

Peter sat on the sofa, unable to return her tirade with the effectiveness he would want if he had been prepared.

'But, Janette, I think I am in love with you still. You looked more beautiful than ever to me tonight.'

Janette just shook her head and sneered. Peter held his head in his hands and ran his fingers slowly back through his greying hair.

In silence, they both went to their separate bedrooms.

After breakfast, a week after this argument, Peter deliberately held his Audi back in the layby on the road outside their perfect house, watching to see what Janette's movements would be on her day off work. Stephen Sanders's car came down the road towards him and then turned into the driveway. Peter watched as his wife came out to meet him, leaving the front door, looking more dangerously elegant than he could recall ever seeing before. She kissed Stephen on the lips and then they embraced with their whole bodies, got into the car and drove away.

Peter started his car up as if to follow them, but instead of putting the car in gear he turned on the radio on. On Radio 2, the beginning notes of the Kinks' 'Death of a Clown' came on. He sat there as if paralysed, and looked across at his once-perfect house.

It was still the first half of the morning and the day was bright and promising. It was still August and there was plenty of potential left for a beautiful end to the summer. Everything around Peter was promising and had picture-postcard beauty about it. Cheshire fields and hay bales in the late summer morning sun.

Yet Peter felt empty inside. He turned the radio up louder, opened the sun roof and drove to work. He watched everything around him happening with more clarity and intensity than he had before. He knew that he could never undo his mistakes and he knew that he would be trapped by his devotion and his cowardice for the rest of his life.

TOMORROW'S SKY

'Until there is a home for everyone.'

Shelter (the UK's leading homelessness
and housing charity)

I was a working-class boy from a Protestant neighbourhood. I loved and collected rhythm-and-blues records. I fell in love with Nicola from when we first spoke slowly to each other at school. She was rich and I was poor. She was cold and I was hot. I was in love with her. She wasn't in love with me, but she liked me a lot when it suited her, and particularly when I was showing her lots of attention. Her smile was perfect and genuine and could light up the air around her. She had read widely and had a worldliness and desire for spontaneity and adventure in music, arts and travel that captivated me and belied her fourteen years. For one month we were lovers and she never looked at another boy.

Oh, to be born again. If I ventured in the slipstream, between the viaducts of your dreams. And if I could talk to Huddie Ledbetter – he understood what rejection was like. He understood what it was like to be an outsider. All of those people pointing a finger at me and him and whispering behind our backs in the hall.

I hope you are OK, Nicola. I hope you are taking good care of your little boy, seeing that he has clean clothes and putting on his little red shoes. Would you kiss my eyes? And lay me down easily until I drift way up above you to my home on high? I belong in another time, I belong in another place, I belong in another face…

I was traumatised because I didn't fit in. I wasn't like everybody else in Nicola's world. All the other boys she was associated with had rich parents, stable career prospects and the confidence and swagger of the upper classes. I just had my rock-and-roll 45s. And Yeats. And Eliot. And Behan.

My friend Little Jimmy has deserted me forever now. And that other character, Broken Arrow, has a plan and a final destination for me. All of the dogs are barking for me. My death is coming, way down on the diamond-studded highway where you wander, Nicola, and over onto the railroad tracks. The scrapbooks of our childhood photos together are stuck with glue. The dynamo of your smile caressed the barefoot virgin child in me. And there you are now, high on your high-flying cloud, looking down at the childhood lover that you have left effortlessly behind.

Young romantic love is pure and simple. Nicola on her own is pure and simple. When it is just me and her together, it is perfect. We can exist in isolation in a way that would make us both happy forever. But then her disapproving family and patronising Irish friends gatecrash our love and throw stones through the glass. I want to escape from this world. I need to leave Belfast and I want to escape my existence. I want transcendence through rock and roll. She will never marry a boy like me.

She will never meet another boy like me ever again. Take me to Tír na nóg.

In my dreams, I stroll across the emerald island, drinking clear clean water to quench my thirst. I watch out for ferry boats on the blue sea and look upwards for tomorrow's sky. Tomorrow's sky is where I want to go to as I wander through other people's gardens, all misty and wet with rain. She doesn't love me; she told me this in a coffee house and I would rather die than live on this earth without her love. I will never grow so old again as when I used to walk around the neighbourhood with her on my arm.

'I perhaps don't feel the same way as you,' she told me coldly at a restaurant table.

That's just fine. I guess I will have to be eternally satisfied not to read between the lines. We part ways near the theatre and she hugs me with condescending rejection in her bones. Her and her champagne eyes and her saint-like smile.

Sex follows love sometimes. Sometimes sex happens without love. Sometimes love happens without sex. Sometimes when they happen together it can scare you and make you want to run away. I was conquered in a car seat by Nicola, and it affected me more deeply than it affected her, I think. It scared me as I was too young to understand it. It was my first time. It wasn't her first time. She took my 'Cyprus Avenue' virginity. And then I ran away and never came back.

I may go crazy before that mansion on the hill, as the leaves fall one by one. I shout out at the autumn time and call it a fool. I cannot speak to any other girls after the rejection – my tongue just gets tied and my insides shake. I go to the river alone and get drunk on cherry wine. I pine for her and pine for her. We were both fourteen years old.

In my dreams Nicola and I are together. A wedding together. A child together. But it is just a dream and I wake up. For the first twenty seconds the dream seems real and then the cold harshness of reality hits me and my body trembles with fear. I no longer have my friend Broken Arrow. I no longer have my stream-of-consciousness thoughts of love and tenderness. The loss of innocence and the fourteen-year-old girl. I should be back in school, but I listen to the Small Faces instead.

I take many different jobs and the years pass and pass. On my days off, I stroll through the fields. I just want to kiss her one more time, like young lovers. I want us to go to the dance together, like we did that time. Such a perfect-looking couple on a summer evening, with our parents proud of us and hopeful that we might end up as sweethearts forever.

Homeless now, a vagabond now. Drifting from place to place and drinking to numb the pain. The pain that Nicola will never be mine. She was mine on Cyprus Avenue, but now that moment is long gone and I fucked it up so much that we will never be together again. Instead, a transvestite befriends me and I become entranced by the duality and the otherworldliness. I realise that we are so similar and connected. Madam George becomes my friend, Madam George becomes my lover, Madam George becomes my world for now.

She appears like a childlike vision, leaping into view. Down on Cyprus Avenue. A tall glamorous transsexual with her clicking and clacking high-heeled shoe. Many of the soldier boys love her and fulfil their silent fantasies with her. I just talk to her and tell her everything of Nicola and the love we once had as she lets her sweet smell of perfume drift over me. She counsels and consoles me and hypnotises me some nights into a deep trance. On other nights, we play dominoes until she gets scared and leaves me alone again.

'Lord have mercy, I think it's the cops.'

And she leaves and takes the train up from Dublin to Sandy Row. We cannot travel on public transport together, she tells me, and her voice deepens. Madam George is the only person I care for now that I know I cannot be with Nicola. The life of a drag queen is hard though and she cannot fully let me into everything. She has secrets that she will always keep from me I guess. She has to get on the train and I have to say goodbye to the tall, angular and beautiful Madam George.

I have left the past behind me now. I have fallen into a trance. Yet still I see Nicola. I experience hallucinations and I see a beautiful adult Nicola at the peak of her success. The ballerina. Was that her walking past me last week in the snow as I begged for change, on the arm of a man twice her age? Was that her laughing, excited and full of life? Doing all she can to impress the older man. Was that her? Did she throw me a glance? And a second glance? Did our eyes meet? Did she know it was me in the snow and homeless on the corner of the street? Did she fly on by just like a ballerina?

I sleep on the road outside a lonely twenty-two-storey block. No one chooses to be homeless. No one chooses to have their heart broken forever by a cruel ballerina.

It is getting late and I ring the bell and see who answers. Then I stand in the doorway and start mumbling and I cannot remember the last thing that ran through my head

The last day I remember, I stood in Nicola's doorway and her friend opened the door. Was that Nicola upstairs? Did I see my love or was I hallucinating again? I tried to talk but I froze up and said nothing. My well-rehearsed pitch that I had been over and over with Jimmy on Cyprus Avenue all day disappeared like a column of breath into the Belfast night. It all happened in slow motion and I walked away knowing it was my last day on this earth.

Like a slim slow slider, I saw you walking past Ladbroke Grove this morning. You are out of my reach and you wouldn't even recognise me now. You have your brand-new boy and your Cadillac. I have my alcohol addiction, the long hair covering my weather-beaten face and my home on the pavement.

'Nicola!' I cry out at tomorrow's sky. Nobody answers. And the alcohol isn't strong enough for me now, so I need to go to the next level.

I get caught up on dope and blonde, beautiful ballerina Nicola is gone forever. Winter comes down and then death. Death on the cold streets. Being homeless forever is like death. When you walk past me, somewhere within the homeless boy sat by the cashpoint and the alcohol and the polite requests for spare change, is the deepest and purest love you will ever know.

ALIVE

'The flame of complete combustion has a blue tinge. It is a beautiful colour; it is a ferocious colour. A piece of writing is powerful if its words are completely combusted.'

Chen Yizhi

'I think I want to grow up to be a rock star,' the sandy-haired, chubby-faced young boy said to his motionless teacher, who was babysitting him whilst his parents went gallivanting out on the pier and then took late-night moonlit swims and tried to fuck in the ocean. Toxic shock syndrome was something you had to rail against if you wanted to break free from a conservative neighbourhood.

'You are sure of that, aren't you?'

The teacher thought the boy to be good-looking and harboured considerable jealousy towards the comfortable life he had – the carefree parents devoid of puritanical morality and his natural good looks at such a young age. It was a far cry from the speech impediment, the acne, the dandruff and the bad breath that were so common in children that age, he thought to himself angrily.

'Yeah, I can communicate with dead rock stars, you know. They talk to me from up in Heaven. Jim Morrison does, Jimi Hendrix does and Jeff Buckley does too.'

The boy uttered these words so confidently that all the teacher could do was to stab a knife firmly and defiantly into the boy's stomach five minutes later. It was done with the confidence of a celebrity chef preparing a meal that they had cooked dozens of times before.

Until this point, the teacher had been without sin. A virginal life steeped in Catholicism and tradition. Rosaries, Hail Marys and confessions, stacked up in a seamless LinkedIn profile of praise and recommendations.

Now he knew he would go to Hell, and so he kept plunging the knife into the dead boy's stomach and watching blood spurt across the white kitchen floor, like a Spanish tomato festival.

'He never would have been a rock star,' the teacher muttered to himself as the boy's parents returned from their midnight swim in the ocean, wrapped in towels and drinking mojitos, totally unaware of the kitchen bloodshed they were about to return to.

The teacher walked away from the house and onto a road heading out east to the Pacific Highway.

'Besides,' he muttered to himself, 'it is 2020 now, and rock and roll died out a long time ago.'

GEORGE FLOYD

I don't want to live in this world any more
I just watched George Floyd die
Under the knee of a white supremacist cop
With three other cops watching on
And they calmly let it all happen
And put him in the ambulance
I can't breathe
I can't breathe
My neck hurts
Everything hurts
I want my mama

I don't want to live in this world any more
If the leaders of the free world
Are allowing this to happen in 2020
After everything that has gone on before
Has there been any real progress?
I went on the march in Manchester
And kissed Becky at Oxford Road Station
To try and do something and feel something
To break from the inertia and the apathy

To try and believe that a better future can be built
But I keep coming back to the image of defenceless George
I can't breathe
I can't breathe
My neck hurts
Everything hurts
I want my mama

I don't want to live in this world anymore
If God created Derek Chauvin
I want no part of religion
If God says to me 'All Lives Matter'
I am going to punch him in the face
I don't want to live in this world anymore

BUDDY HOLLY, YOU DON'T HAVE TO DIE

Buddy Holly, you don't have to die
You don't have to board that plane today
The Winter Dance Party
Of February 1959
Won't set the world alight
We could have survived without it
But these last sixty-one years we have struggled to survive
*   without you*
You could have stayed alive
Toured England again
To places like Swindon, Preston or Nottingham
The rock-and-roll outposts
You could have stayed alive
And written more words of love
To sustain us through the decades
And when someone wrote in graffiti on that wall
'Buddy Holly Lives'
It would have been the truth
Because one day truth and justice will reign
Keep on walking down that Jericho Road
Keep on walking down that Jericho Road

Through the cities of immigrants
Keep writing new music and keep touring
Show Elvis Presley up as a sell-out
Controlled by Colonel Tom Parker
Not the free spirit that you are
Damn it, why did Robert Johnson make that pact with the Devil
Toss the coin again
Maybe Waylon gets on that plane instead
Or maybe the plane doesn't take off at all
Take a break, lads, from chasing your own little mouse trails
And feeding the promoters and managers their money
Take a break and make some new music in a wooden hut in the wilderness
For 'Peggy Sue', forever ago
Your number-one singles don't have to be posthumous
It doesn't matter anymore
You just don't have to get on that plane, Buddy Holly
You don't have to die!

CLARKSDALE

Needed to create a pact with the Devil
To ensure the greatest music of the future
I fell down on my knees
And a bad-luck gale has been blowing ever since

I killed them all by the way with my wicked deal
Buddy Holly, Eddie Cochran, Marc Bolan
I flew your plane into the ground
I drove your cars all the way to collision
Devil may speak to me
Devil may seduce me
Devil may care

No one is going to mess with my head no more
With the number thirteen tattooed on my arm
I created this pact
Without it you would never have heard 'Moonlight Mile'
Or smashed up your bedroom to the Sex Pistols
Or stayed in your room all weekend studying Blonde on
    Blonde
So I take a bow

You can thank me now
Devil may speak to me
Devil may seduce me
Devil may care
The Devil cared alright and lit up your life with meteoric brilliance
I was born in Hazlehurst to bring trouble to you!

THE FACES OF MY ENEMIES

I lie in bed on a Saturday morning
And I don't want the day to come
I see the faces of my enemies when I close my eyes
They come to me relentlessly in my dreams
Many of them now, tormenting and trying to break me
I feel like a soldier of fortune
Dealing with his own post-traumatic stress
Reminded nightly of his lawless and godless ways
Reminded nightly of his cavalier and wild days
The wreckage, oh the wreckage
I am waiting at the traffic lights, waiting for you
Where are you?

When will I stop seeing the faces of my enemies
In my nightmares and hidden memories?
Shipwrecks make great paintings
Car crashes make great plot twists
Gotta get through this
Like a soldier of fortune
Until you show up and get in the passenger seat
Like Dominic Cummings, not sure if you are my friend or
  enemy

136

In these strange times of fake news and fake people
The lights go green and we will drive into the sunset
On a one-way ticket to the jetty
And a boat that will take both of us to the New World

YOUR FAN CLUB
(DEDICATED TO KATHLEEN BRENNAN)

I am your relentless, self-loathing, adoring apprentice
Writing poems about you
Thinking about you constantly
Drowning myself in vodka
And dedicating rock-and-roll records to you
On Boogie Street

I am the devoted, driven and dangerously obsessed leader of
    your fan club
Defending you always
Against all the false allegations
Spreading your fame
Perpetuating your myth
With religious fervour like Little Richard
On Boogie Street

I am your visceral, amphetamine-popping, crazed obsessive
Full of love for your energy and creativity
Like the collision of Velvet Underground and Nico
In naked 1967
Like 'Step On Inside' by Vietnam
Just when we both thought rock and roll might be drawing its
    last breath
We were so wrong
On Honky Tonk Street

I am your deluded and deranged poet laureate groupie
Damned and addicted to your hypnotic smile
I will invent worlds for you to prolong your great legends
Like Enobarbus, I know I am under a spell I cannot escape
from
Fixing to die
Fixing to live
Fixing fixing fixing
Fixing up a right raucous royal rock-and-roll revolution for
you
Every day of the week in my head
And then I will unravel and you will see me laid bare
My darling
A little bit Beale Street, Memphis
A little bit Bourbon Street, New Orleans
A little bit Matthew Street, Liverpool
A little bit Sauchiehall Street, Glasgow
A little bit Canal Street, Manchester
A little bit Bleecker Street, Greenwich Village
A little bit AC/DC Lane, Melbourne
I feel so alive with you
Every day of the week in my head
Every day of the week in my head
On Boogie Street

THE NEW KILLERS

I am too old to talk now to the new killers
In the nightclubs
And the late-night bars
I don't know what they drink these days
I don't know what they dance to these days
Severin Severin awaits me there

I am tired and I am weary
I get tongue-twisted and my stutter kicks in
The boy in the bubble once again
Different colour shades made from my tears
Appear in my mind
As if I was in the UFO Club on Tottenham Court Road
The Whiplash Girl appears before me
And I stand and stare
She isn't really there
In reality there are just swarms and swarms of the new killers
Who wouldn't understand my lament

And so I leave the nightclub
With an unheralded fire escape exit
And run fast into the night
Like I have committed a crime
And you and I know that I have
My demons rise up the faster I run
Away from the crowded streets I can run faster now
Long loping 'don't-look-at-me-I-am-a-madman' strides
And still die young if I want to
Like a double fantasy moment
Oh mercy for me
I can do anything I want to
Just keep me away from
The new killers

ALTAMONT SPEEDWAY

The greatest decade in the history of humanity
Is soon about to end
How dare it
How horrible to think that time is fleeting
And we will never live in that decade again
The records of the Beatles, Bob Dylan, the Kinks and the
    Rolling Stones
The Velvet Underground and Nico
The first two Led Zeppelin albums
The Doors' first album
All three Jimi Hendrix Experience albums
Pet Sounds
Astral Weeks
Tommy
Everybody Knows This Is Nowhere
How dare it all end
I can't take it
I became a Hell's Angel in California
But where do I go from here?

The sixth of December 1969
Bad acid everywhere
The innocence of Monterey lost
The overrated Woodstock has happened

I saw my buddies take on members of the Jefferson Airplane
With pool cues and tyre irons
The Stones played 'Sympathy for the Devil'
'Gimme Shelter'
'Street Fighting Man'
Violence and menace in every song
And the bad acid around me
And the drinking around me
All it takes for evil to happen
Is for a good man (like me) to do nothing
'Under My Thumb'
A misogynistic song
'Bad Karma'
And metres from me Meredith Hunter is killed by my buddies
A black man killed by a rain of stabs from knife-wielding
   Angels
I could have stopped it
My guilt stays with me forever
I killed the sixties
The dream is over
And through the seventies I will always be haunted
Unable to regain what I had before
My own constant albatross from Altamont Speedway

BERLIN MELTDOWN

A meltdown was always on the cards
Around May 1976
A Nazi salute at Victoria Station
Could be interpreted any way you wanted
Thin White Duke
Your world on a wing
Portraying Himmler's sacred realm

But this Homo sapiens *hadn't outgrown his use*
You needed a change of scenery
A change of pace
A change of headspace
And the teachings of the Armenian mystic Gurdjieff

No Golden Dawn
More the Crown of Creation
As you became Prospero
And surrounded yourself with books in Berlin
An exorcism of the mind
An exorcism of self
Doing your own shopping
Walking around unnoticed
Hanging out with the Jean Genie

In Berlin you realised how much you hated the Nazis
And the sons of real SS men sorted your head out

LOT 65, GRAVE C

A man drowning in a lake
Caustic, cold, spit it out, Curly
A man drinking whiskey on a railway track
Holy Joe reading the Bible
A boy drowning in the sea
Calling out to me daily over the tidal winds
A girl dying in her sleep
The intense humming of evil
I recognise dim elements of creation
As I stand over your grave
I know that life can get better
No more suspicious mini-deaths of the soul
Lot 65, Grave C

RAVEN'S WILD YEARS

Raven bought a house out in Ashton-Under-Lyne
And she hung her wild years on the nail she drove through her
    client's foreskin
Private school boy
Trans dominatrix extraordinaire
No mockery or ridicule for you in the new woke normal, baby

She walked her dog in the pouring rain
Through the Manchester sewers on Portuguese heels
And drank bourbon with her wife whilst sitting on the dead
    man's chest
She would never marry
But took days off to go the carnival
Get the money up front
A couple of fifty-pound notes make it dark inside her chambers
Salamanders slither and blood will spill
She pretends to be a Dutch orphan
And her memory is like a jet plane

One night Raven lined up all her wealthiest clients
Gathered them into a dungeon and ordered them all to take
their clothes off
Pulling a pistol from her mistress boots
She shot them one by one
Poured herself a White Russian
And started reading her Edgar Allan Poe book whilst laughing
repetitively
Everything was black, orange and pink in her world
Yesterday was not here, she realised
What would tomorrow bring?

SHE STANDS OVER MY GRAVE

She stands over my grave
Knowing only she could have saved me
The death penalty still exists in my state
She was my alibi
When I was accused of the heinous crime I didn't commit

It couldn't have been me
Because that night I was in her arms
She shamefully blows kisses at my headstone
And I watch back as a plain-clothed jailbird
Who is keeping a wildebeest in his headache

She stands over my grave
As my best friend's wife
So maybe I deserved the chair for other reasons
That Robert Johnson could tell you about
She walks slowly through the graveyard
To the mansion where she makes love to her husband that
*   night.*

THE PEACOCK

Charlie the Peacock wanders aimlessly
Through the orchard of the house I grew up in
Never a fear
Never a deathly thought
Behind those grey eyes
Yet in his body is stored
All the knowledge of my future life
All the triumphant stories
All the mistakes I made

Charlie the Peacock drew pentagrams
And occasionally shed feathers
Near the kidney-shaped pond I jumped over
Never take the feathers into the house
Or bad things will happen in the future
Created by Charlie
As he sets out his plans for me
And I never see a live peacock again
Anchored by other superstitions after the age of nine

Seagulls circling endlessly over my head
As I sit on the Bracklesham Bay shingle
Warning me late at night with silent harmonies
When I thought no one was watching
To leave this country and grow my own future
With another canny peacock walking serenely through my
  orchard

2020 BLUES

Here I am in 2020, baby
I gotta say it ain't as cool as I thought it was gonna be
Can't go to the pub, watch a live game or even get a kiss
What in the hell would Woody Guthrie make of all of this?

An invisible virus has kidnapped the world's cities
Too much time on my own now to write my self-obsessed ditties
Lights out in the heart of America
No love in a time of media hysteria
Can't go to a café, sit on a park bench or even get a kiss
What in the hell would Buddy Holly make of all this?

Where the hell is the flying car I am owed
Road? Where we are going we don't need a road...
Living on Zoom calls and working from home
Sat in the garden as a reinvented laughing gnome
Can't go to a restaurant, visit a friend or even get a kiss
What in the hell would Hank Williams make of all of this?

Now social distancing will haunt us all for years
I am becoming an introvert, still getting in the beers
Guess I still got my books, movies and a hillbilly tune
Let's just hope that lockdown gets lifted by June
Can't go on a date, drive a car or even get a kiss
What in the hell would Townes Van Zandt make of all of this?

TEAR DOWN ALL THE RACIST STATUES

Tear down all the racist statues
Edward Colston, you had to be toppled
Tear down all the racist statues
Cecil Rhodes, you need to go next
Slavery was our original sin
Apartheid was an abomination
Educate yourself
Read about black history
Challenge the narratives of your parents
Challenge the way history has previously been taught
Search your own past
Go deeply into your own prejudices and fears
Tear it all down and start again
And build something on compassion and love
Kindness is not a weakness
Fight bigotry, injustice and inequality
Until the haters have all been drowned out
Until a New World becomes the norm

ECHO AND THE CAMPAIGNERS

Her name was Echo
With Irish freckles
And a Germanic poise
She loved Greta Thunberg
She was so switched on it impressed me all week long
Up in your arms must be a great place to be
Oh fate!

Echo travels the world
And takes on all the challenges thrown at her
No man will dilute her passion ever
She has her own inner strength to stay single
She is like a sailboat
On silver or crystal-blue water
When the waves grow higher
She stays firm and upright
As if protected by an invisible anchor

There are crystals of salt
In the corners of her mouth
I can see them

But no one will taste it
As she goes out and fights for what she makes
Tells the uninformed and apathetic
That our big brands
Cannot exploit the female garment workers
Of Bangladesh
Of Cambodia
Of Vietnam
Of China
There must be transparency
And they must be paid a living wage

I know your daddy loves you, Echo
Loves Ocean Rain and Heaven Up Here
He helped to create a strong soul
A resolute reminder of all that is good in the world
Quietly and profoundly I am declaring
That I am a freak (you knew that already)
And I am in love with Echo
And what she makes

I AM HIROSHIMA

I wanted to call my daughter Hiroshima
I wanted to call my band Hiroshima
I even considered calling you Hiroshima

Hiroshima

The darkest, deadliest and most evil thing that we all conspired to
We created a nuclear bomb to remind us that the Devil is real
We dropped the bomb to admit all our failings
And we have glossed over it
And created history books and black-and-white films
Of heroes and villains
And perpetuated the lie for seventy-five years

I cannot bear the lies any more
I want the whole world to say sorry
For the silent suffering
For silent suffering endures eternally
And clarifies the Beast that we want to pretend does not exist

And so from today I am calling myself Hiroshima

TRYING TO BE WALT WHITMAN

Who is carrying the crucifix today, little sister?
Thou shalt not fall
I saw the autumn leaves
I saw the childhood memories at the Catholic junior school
I remember the Saturday masses
I remember the conker fights
I remember the details of the science lessons

And some of those teachers
Who were never fully qualified
To teach a twentieth-century boy
Are lost now in their retirements
Harking back to the seventies and eighties
And getting confused by Facebook
And what to write and not to write
In case a thread starts to feel like Operation Yewtree
When there was none of that in those innocent days

Who is carrying the crucifix, little brother?
Thou shalt not fall
I just don't know what to do with myself
When the early days had structure and meaning
And I don't think I ever had doubts in the Spinney

Or questioned the meaning of life on lonely long-distance runs
I had camaraderie
And I learnt volumes every day
And I had my books and my sporting heroes
And I carried a crucifix of death
And went to confession
And listened to Beatles albums for the first time

Dear diary,
How do I find a magic cure
For the feelings of longing and belonging and nostalgia
How do I recreate the glory days at a wooden desk
In a Smith Street bar
With a dimming lamp
And a Pausefest flyer on the table
A White Light Australian Vodka bottle filled with foam pieces
And a wilted rose protruding aimlessly from its mouth
And the monotonous car alarm going off outside
Confusing the musical codas in my brain, little sister
Yet creating in my mind the city aura of the Beat Generation

There is only one solution – write for love!
There is only one ending I want – identify with love and write
  for love!

SURROUNDED BY KALBARRI GYPSIES

You probably thought that Robin Hood was long gone
But he lives!
In Western Australia
He didn't die for anyone's sins
He hasn't been back to Nottingham for a while
He hasn't seen Maid Marian walking so fine down the street
*   in a while*
He is surrounded by Kalbarri gypsies
And he never tires of them
Shark Bay is his new Sherwood Forest
Pops down to Geraldton
From time to time
Doesn't steal from the rich right now
But could do if needed – twisting tormented lullabies appear
*   in Robin's brain*
He never tires of the sea
And will defend the Aboriginal people
And the Torres Strait Islander people
From any oppressor
If you choose inaction, he says
You have chosen the side of the oppressor

He wants to close the gap
But he takes drugs now
And his revolution is in hibernation
Yet in his bones
There is the art of song
And he needs you, reader, to reawaken him
What he stands for will never die
His spirit is just sleeping in Western Australia for a while

THE MAY QUEEN

The May Queen banishes winter's icicles
And carries fire
For a future unwritten
Believe in the power of the May Queen
Every year she is there for you
Every day she will save you from your demons

Surrender now to the May Queen (of Robert Plant)
And when her task is done
She will disappear and run her glorious bordello
With friends (who are your friends too)
And smile kindly as she exits stage left
Whilst you focus on matters at hand
Back in the game, lover boy
Back in the game, you beautiful mess
One Voice Fundraising is yours

As you were, my friend

I DON'T WANNA GROW UP

I have been getting away with it so much recently
Dancing through life in hours of longing
But it's gonna hit me like a freight train soon
Forties coming on strong
I don't wanna grow up

Ladies and gentlemen
Here is my gloomy spoiler alert
Give me a standing ovation
And then I will rub my face in the dirt
I don't wanna grow up

I would take all of my tomorrows
All of the phoney flirting, all of the accumulation of wealth
Even all of your love
And trade it all in for one of my yesterdays
I don't wanna grow up

If I had made a different phone call
We never would have met
If I had walked to a different bar that night
We never would have met
If I had trusted in my gut and intuition
We never would have met
If I had woken up an hour later
We never would have met
If the other girl had kissed me and taken me home
We never would have met

Feed your head, feed your head, feed your head
Whilst you can
With all the wondrous madness and chaos around you
Let's be lovers
You and me
As long as you accept that I don't wanna grow up

DRIVING HOME LATE

I saw the dead man lying by the side of the road
As I was driving home late
In the June gloaming
No one else was around that night
Just me and the dead man

I let my car pull to a gentle stop
And I stood up and stared at him in his grey suit on the
  pavement
In his fifties, I would guess
And dressed for his work like Mister Clean
It's always better on holiday
Everything seems much better when you are on holiday

I looked around at the dark green country around me
No breathing, no humans, no sign of any movement
There was the white lines painted on the country road
There was my blue car
There was the red of a summer sunset on the horizon
But everything else was dark green
He looked so still and peaceful
And I wanted to die too

For five minutes I watched and waited
And deliberated with my mobile phone
He looked so happy

But he was so dead
That nothing could save him now
He had found something that I had been searching for all my life
And the sky went redder still
Like bloodstains when they first appear in your day
And you know that every day is claustrophobic
And you are running
Running to be free
Free from the pain of life

The dead man's face had a beautiful smile
And I wanted to lie down next to him
But I wasn't in my working clothes
And my casually clothed disguise had fooled no one now
I was Mr Dirty
And it was only me and him that knew the beautiful truth
As the night came down
And the sparrows and bats started circling us

I walked back into my blue car
And drove my suicide machine home to my family
And to the daily lies that engulfed my life
And I never told a word to anyone until now
About the night I spent with a dead man lying by the side of
   the road.

THE TRUTH WILL NEVER BE REVEALED

The truth will never be revealed
That is the truth
It's a fine line between a good life and a life in jail
How does the mirror look to you right now?
You chose to throw me to the dogs
Because you believed a liar

The truth will never be revealed
That is the truth
I cannot prove anything
All I have is my actions
And a clear memory
It must be easier for you to stick to your routined life
And act as the great defender of mist and veils
To protect yourself from any criticism from your peers
Make me a scapegoat
For your cowardice

Keep on training
Like Magwitch
Keep on recruiting
Like Charles Manson
Keep on managing
Like Don Revie
Keep on innovating
Like Status Quo
Stay within your well-defined limitations
And don't ever fucking talk to me again.

LIVING LIKE A TIBETAN MONK

I want to live the rest of my life like a Tibetan monk
And wear one of those magnificent robes
And find my inner peace
And meditate daily
And bring calm and love to all around me

I want to live the rest of my life like a Tibetan monk
But I have worn down the knuckle too far
And I fear that it is too late now
Too late to never thrust again
Too late to never lust again
Too late to never bust again
I still watch Pornhub in my room on a Tuesday night
And think of a Welsh dominatrix in my quiet mind
As I start to fade in and out of sleep
When will this all stop?

Maybe I need to move to Liverpool
And get a nine-to-five job
And drink hard on Matthew Street every blurring weekend
And chase desire
And live for thrills
Gamble, drink and fuck
Into my fifties
And make Charles Bukowski proud
And forget all that Tibetan monk nonsense!

INDEPENDENT HEAD

Hey there, Independent Head
I think a little bit of you died when you left Liverpool
You ran to the outside
And embraced a topsy-turvy ride
And met men you didn't understand
(What was there to understand though?)

You know what I think of you, Independent Head?
I love the old you
And you should return to your roots
Stimulate the G-spot of your heart
Don't follow the leader
Or obey the laws of gravity
TV dreams can confuse
Long hours alone in your hotel room
Make you sad now
Thinking about the positive foetus you once were
And the negative corpse of your denials

Stop thinking so much
Get back inside
Get Zen and the Art of Scouse Republic Maintenance
Go back to the Krazyhouse
Or Heebee Jeebies
Or the Rubber Soul Bar
And meet me there
And we can spend blissful hours
Talking about the confusions that once rained down on our
*   lives*

SIOBHAN KNOWS

Siobhan knows me better than the rest
She saw me at my peak
When I handcuffed the dancing winds
And she saw me at my lowest depths
When the thought of a hangover could drive me suicidal

Siobhan is there for me
Consistent and resilient like Swiss clockwork
With purple streaks in her hair
Painting night-time colours
That motivate me to see the world in a new way
Siobhan owns the writer's skull
And future generations
Belong to this Irish banshee and her hypnotic counsel

ROOM 516

It makes a lot of sense to just disappear
Disappearance is a lot more mysterious than suicide
Like Richey Manic
When he checked out of room 516

He didn't want to be like Cobain
And join the twenty-seven club properly
He didn't like joining clubs
Drive out of London
Back to Blackwood
Then the Severn View service station
Gave us all the idea

I could disappear now too
From this tropical island
With the touts and their lizards
And the massage girls and their happy endings
A happy ending
Could be to disappear completely
Where no one could ever find me
And live happily away from pressures

Away from expectations
Away from the conformist cowards
And just talk to God in my head when I need to
And guarantee a happy ending.
Sex with a groupie in Camden Town

I once had sex with a groupie in Camden Town
Up near the Barfly
She thought I was someone else
And for a short while so did I

I wore lots of make-up
Lots of eyeliner
And was heavily tattooed
I had a crucifix around my neck
And I thought I was someone else for a while

'Are you a Libertine?' she asked me
I just smiled menacingly
And her tongue went to work
Tasting of oil and nicotine
Like a first kiss
In a Pamplona San Fermin Fiesta bar
With 'Paradise City' blaring out to the crowds

Camden Town had Rehearsal Rehearsals
And the Britpop crowds at the Good Mixer
I had the groupie's salty tongue
And we fucked in a toilet
In a doggy-style position
Without a condom
And other people could hear
But we didn't get thrown out

Normal people have girlfriends
Normal people can love other people
I just keep applying the eyeliner
And I think I am someone else every day now.

UP ON THE MOORS

They did unspeakable things to their still-warm corpses
Oh Manchester
Still so much to answer for
A hastily glued together visual and sensory explosion of torn-
*   out pictures*
Wendy James
Rudolf Hess
Stuart Sutcliffe
Randall Stevens
Sydney Carton
Krystal Swift
Does anybody remember these people?
Or what they had in common?

Up on the moors you can escape
You can disappear like in The Vanishing
No one judges you up there
And the rain feels good falling on your head
You wouldn't use an umbrella
Or a laptop
Or a mobile phone
You would walk in silence
And find peace
And eliminate the chattering voices in your head.

CARVE YOUR NAME INTO MY ARM

I just met you tonight in a Koh Samui bar
Near the loud music and the Connect 4 girls
In Henry Africa's bar of escapist terror
Carve your name into my arm. will you please?
'Sorry, are you crazy?'
'Yes I am. Carve your name into my arm, please'

Those who want to fight...
Let them fight.
And those who do not want to fight in this world of eternal
*   struggle...*
Do not deserve to live

You look like a stand-out person in here
Someone real
Amongst the fake hippies and the sex tourists
Amongst the touts and the robotic lipstick traces
So please...
Give me good copy
I will feel no pain this time
Please just carve your name slowly but clearly into my
*   beautiful forearm*

Once you have done that I will happily reject society
Like Salinger
And go and live in a concrete bunker.

REWIND THERAPY

I think you are going to need rewind therapy
That was what she told me
My counsellor sitting in the narrow, vicious room.
To get over what you have been through
You will need to relive it again and again and again
Watch yourself watching yourself watching yourself
On a TV screen on a DVD.
You will have the remote controls to everything that happened
And be able to play, fast forward and rewind
And play, fast forward and rewind
Over and over again
Through all the shock
Navigating your way through the turbines in your mind
Until you finally come to rest on the winter beach.

We are going to do it over and over again
It will affect your sleep and give you nasty dreams
You may even feel you are bipolar for a while
As chemical collisions corrode your consciousness.

But the rewind therapy will work
And in the future you will walk free
A taller and happier man.

In the narrow and vicious room I consent
Knowing I can always go and hang out in Raves from the
    Grave afterwards.

SPECTATOR OF SUICIDE

I never died in the end
I kept on living
Something pulled me through
Something told me I wasn't Ian Curtis
Something told me I wasn't Richey Edwards
I was going to become a spectator of suicide instead

When they attacked the Muslims
I decided to stand up for them
When they attacked the transgender people
I decided to stand up for them
When they attacked the homeless
I decided to stand up for them
When they attacked the prostitutes
I decided to stand up for them

Under my happy-go-lucky demeanour
Hells tides continually run
I dance with the delinquents
I am on trial and I am in prison every day that passes
Like Lucifer I
Will board that plane to America
Handcuffed to a smiling train
And a Brooklyn 7-Eleven
That could finally set me free

DREAMS OF NICK DRAKE

He only released three albums
He didn't like performing live
And he sold few records in his lifetime
Yet his legend grows and grows
I think about him most days
I have looked on Zoopla
At house prices in Tanworth-in-Arden
I have listened over and over to Five Leaves Left
And to Pink Moon
And to 'Rider on the Wheel'
What was going on in Nick Drake's head?

He was a surfer riding opiate waves
Three hours from sundown
He broke through old England's wall of impenetrable stoicism
And taught us of the 'River Man'
His songs have seeped into my bone marrow
And lodged deep in my vital organs
They symbolise something undefined in me
Akin to magic
'One of These Things First'
'The Thoughts of Mary Jane'
'Black Eyed Dog'

His illness was a hunting animal
A morphine ocean dragging him away from us all
Nick Drake will live within me always

TAKE ME TO THE SEA

When black thunder-clouds arrive in your brain
God will arrive on time, I hope
And my advice is to head down to the sea

Take me to the sea
Take me to Rhossili Bay
Clacton-on-Sea, Lowestoft, Great Yarmouth or Port Ferrin
Dr Syntax's Head, Logan Rock, Megavissey or Saltash
Porth Ferrin, Newquay, Redruth or Kenneggy Downs
(Ruth was always red)

Take me to the sea when my petrol tank is empty
Take me to Porthmadog
Like a mad dog
Tilly Whim Caves, Hastings, Clovelly or Bull Dog Sands
Babbacombe Cliff, Kenfig Sands, My Lord's Rock or
   Shakespeare Cliff
Flashbacks of me, the fool
Tintagel Castle, Shag Rock, Topsham or Dunscombe Cliff
Close your eyes though and pretend there aren't Tories
   everywhere
Hope the beach is deserted

Take me down to the lonesome sea in the morning
Take me to Skegness
Overstrand, Porlock Weir, Canford Cliffs or the Needles
Margam Sands, Bognor Regis, Peacehaven or Dover

Rhyl, Scarborough, Kettle Ness or Deal
And we can finally see who the liar is now
Take me to the sea and play me a Townes Van Zandt album
Take me to Robin Hood's Bay
Whitby, Spaniard Rocks, the Oaze or Shoeberry Ness
Shellness, Sandwich Flats, Nayland Rock or Leysdown-on-Sea
Mablethorpe, Hoylake, Crosby or Southport
I love it up here but, oh God, how did it suddenly get so dark for me?

The roles are reversed now, my lover, and I want to take you to the sea
Take you to Rainy Rock
Frenchman's Bay, Hartlepool, Whitley Bay or Redcar
Oh, the girls of Redcar – oh my!
Morecambe, Maryport, Knockbrex or Dalgety Bay
Troon, Oban, Applecross or the Mull of Kintyre
You need to settle down
Like McCartney I need to settle down too

Take me to the sea and I will marry you one day
Take me to Scarfskerry
Culkein, Kinlochbervie, Tongue House or Badcall
We both of us made a few of those, I suppose
Ramscraigs, Scrabster, Embo or Lossiemouth
St Cyrus, St Monans, Kirkcaldy or Buckie
I did my time in jail all I want you to do now is to take me
  to the sea

Finally take me down to the sea
At Ravenscar
At Cleethorpes
At Burnham Deepdale
Or West Wittering
Better to have loved and lost
A boy on the beach
With a metal detector
Looking for the keys to a heart

GO TO NASHVILLE ONE DAY

I worked for you in Brooklyn Heights
On an album that was a labour of love
So that we could go to Nashville one day
And have people cover the songs we wrote

Songs of betrayal, autobiographical
Filled with real pain, real loves and precious moments
The magical places of Leaves of Grass
We were so poor but we had hope and artistic vision

We would head into Greenwich Village
See Phil Ochs or Bob Dylan on Bleecker Street
One of the great creative periods on Remsen Street
For you and I, life has always been a labour of love

We were only meant to be on this earth for short periods, you
    and I
Everything is not enough and nothing is too much to bear
The strain of rejection starts to weigh heavily
One of us died in the night on a motorcycle
Like a dark joke
The other has many regrets

But the music we made together will live on
And inspire more people's life-novellas hopefully
Born out of a labour of love

BOY FROM THE NORTH COUNTRY

Boy from the North Country
Aspiring Shakespearean actor from Kirkby Lonsdale
We shared a house together
During my own Summer of Love
I was out chasing girls down the Swan
Whilst you had the 'Black Eyed Dog' fixating on you

'I want to shout out that God is love'
You told me in a crowded North London pub
You said you wanted to stand on a table and scream it out
'Don't do that,' I said
What are you, some kind of Manic Street Preacher, boyo?
I knew that your dad was a vicar and was ill
I knew that you were ill
But I didn't understand a Messiah complex
Bipolar depression
Or how I could help you

You were too fragile for fast-paced city life
Living by your own private sense of time
Trying to be a 'pretender', you told me
Your father's illness, your religion and problems with girls
All these things tipped you over the edge

Your death feels like a warning to me
I would say that kindness was your outstanding quality
Get out of the city and away from the poisons
Contemplative solitude breeds a peaceful existence
Alone, alone, alone
And I am happy now in my detachment from the world

OLD MEN IN BETTING SHOPS

Old men in betting shops have got life sussed
I want to be them
They have their own pace of life
Fed to them through a diet of daily excitements
Read the Racing Post *closely every day*
Let yourself go to the armies of emotion
No bosses in the betting shop
No deadlines
No criticisms
No nagging relatives
Comrades to talk to whenever you need them
You can reach your own Buddhist enlightenment
Engross yourself in the races
Create your own tarot cards
Create your own counter-culture
Spend long periods of time in a betting shop every day
And soar up to the sky
Old men in betting shops never die

NOTTINGHAM FOREST BLUES

I grew up here all my life
I can't stay here and I am terrified to leave
I walk down by the River Trent most Saturdays
Feeling those twenty-one years of pain
For John Robertson and Alan Sillitoe I will stay

My parents taught me about that feel
The roar of the crowd as the players run out onto the pitch
The FA Cup in '59 for my wounded dad
Brian Clough's first European Cup for his healing son
For John Robertson and my old man I will stay

Heroes in red give my life structure and routine
When my wife left me for a wealthier man
Success in life is not like success in football
I never wanted to grow up winning cups every year
I just wanted my River Trent walk
My Saturday pint in the Bell Inn on the Market Square
For John Robertson and Robin Hood I will stay

Abused as a child, silenced by my relatives
I tried to escape but the city drew me in
I worked on Upper Parliament Street
And in schools across Chilwell, Old Basford and St Anne's
Always counting down the days to Saturday
To sing my Nottingham Forest Blues
For John Robertson and myself (alone now) I will stay

I have seen them all those managers come and go
Frank Clark, Stuart Pearce and Martin O'Neill
I lost my appetite for sex, love and gambling
I bought Jake Bugg albums, drank in Ye Olde Trip To
   Jerusalem
But the abuse tied itself up unfathomably in my brain
And I find a way to live with it all
By sitting in the Brian Clough Stand for two hours each week
For John Robertson and myself (at peace now) I will stay

A PERSON TO FORGET

How much do you forget in life?
The portraits, the museums, the hollow galleries
I just remember fragments of the early years
The excitement of dark angels passing overhead

How many times did you cry as an adult?
Over the deaths, over the stories, over the heartbreaks
I felt happiest in March 2005; everything seemed possible then
The excitement of dark angels passing overhead

When do you play the game most fearlessly?
When you don't think of failure, or consequences or getting
  arrested
I tried to break every rule in the book
I didn't care at all about money
But fame, I did like that
The excitement of dark angels passing overhead

How would you most like to die?
Seeing as it hasn't happened yet, you could script it
Like John Entwistle

Snorting cocaine off a stripper's naked body
Or of Covid-19, another old man statistic to intensify the
lockdown

She was sixteen years old
And she had never left Arkansas before
But she jumped into the front seat of a car with a red-headed
drifter
To escape her parents' expectations of the lives they wish they
had
She dyed her hair pink
Stopped at various tattoo parlours
Got pregnant to the middle-aged drifter in the back of his car
Drove illegally
Drank Jack Daniels to Janis Joplin's voice
Swam too deep into the Pacific at Ocean Beach
After a day in Cow Records
Her last words pregnant words in the raging riptide were
'No one here gets out alive'

The excitement of dark angels passing overhead

THE ONLY BLACK BOY IN DUBLIN

It puzzled even Al Blue Lewis
When he fought Muhammad Ali in 1972
Where all the black kids in this town?
Ancient worlds, conquered by Vikings and literary greats

Onward over the mountain
I had come to claim the Emerald

And he stands now proudly overlooking Grafton Street
The ultimate outsider
The definition of what Eleanor Roosevelt had said
'No one can make you feel inferior without your consent'

Don't listen to anyone else
Conquer the Emerald your own way
Create your own legend
Don't worry about the people who criticise you at the time
They are probably just jealous of your balls

It's three o'clock in the morning
And I am on the streets of Dublin again
Make your own myths and keep making them until you die
Don't ever retire
Don't ever congratulate yourself too much
Stay hungry
And don't believe a word I tell you
For not a word of this is true

MORTAL COILS

I was always when
And you were always why

These mortal coils disturbed me sporadically
I have cut you out for good now
And thrown you on the funeral pyre
Refugees are now welcome here
Clean-slate happiness – you can purchase it on Amazon

You wrote me so many letters
Gave me great books as presents and signed them too
But you dropped me like hot bricks when it suited you
I was always when
And you were always why

I could achieve superhuman feats
Walk many a country mile for you
Over moors, fields, woods, lanes
Massacre an entire army of Philistines

But on a whim, with no explanation
You could cut my hair
And force me to grinding grain in a mill
Sir Hercules I will become
And I am cutting you out now
Clean-slate happiness – you can purchase it on Amazon
On the thirteenth of April 2020, to be precise
You were why
I was always when

KEEP ON THE WILD SIDE

You need that friction in your life
There is a problem with happiness
Happiness is boring
So keep on the wild side

When you are getting life comfortable
Go get yourself in trouble
With the law and the crowd-pleasers
And keep on the wild side

Don't spend any time counting your money
High-pay cheques lead to apathetic politics
I do my best work when my back is against the wall
So keep on the wild side

For sale, baby's shoes, never worn
Beats the hell out of your dragged-out PhD thesis
That no big-hearted seeker will ever read
Keep on the wild side

VENICE BEACH 2019

How did I get lost
Looking for God on Venice Beach in 2019?
Walking that footpath
Staying away from the exaggerated shops of Abbott Kinney
What mysterious set of life events led me here?

The past is never dead
Wrote William Faulkner
He would have marvelled at the chain of events
From Manchester perfection
Through false allegation
And betrayal
To social alienation
To lack of evidence
Running to stand-still in Dublin
Bad timing
Illness
Lack of health insurance
A snake disguised as a friend
Turning into the Joker in Gotham City

The past is never dead
In Requiem for a Nun
Jim Morrison wrote 'Moonlight Drive' here
And I had been to this spot in many movies
But I had got lost
This is not the warrior I am looking for
This is not the battle I am meant to be fighting
I need to jump off this lonesome train.

TEN-LINE POEM

The consistent burrito sat in the refrigerated area of the fast-
   food restaurant
Surveying all of the activism and action on Union Square
Lauren from South Carolina puts her soul into changing the
   world
She will get there in the end
But her heart needs to find a home first
Don't trust them all, Lauren, stick to the consistent burrito
The others poisoned Phar Lap after the Agua Caliente
   Handicap
The key to this city
Is in the minds of the billion oysters in the harbour
Spying on the misfits and the rebels of the Lower East Side

THE STAIRCASE

Look out, brother
There is a pink moon coming
Coming through the air
With a man from Mars playing 'Ramble Tamble'
Throw in the white towel
There is a man on the stairway
I think you had better call him James
Doesn't look like he is there
To show you burning flames
My apartment is less than a mile away
I hope you come to stay
My room has Marilyn Monroe pictures on the wall
And a gun
We could die there together

Girlfriend has gone
She is a loser in the best clubs
I have been drinking every day
Since the virus crippled the nation
There is a road stretched out between us
And I just turned forty-two
I got nothing else to do
Except press our bodies close together
Look out, brother

Gun in my hand now
As you sleep in summer morning's sweat and blankets

Blankets from Louise, the teenage queen
Red cranberry and vodkas mean run, brother
Bullets mean we are going to fly away together
Our love adds up to nothing
Our parents will never understand
When the first shot is fired
Our morning moment will have peaked

Raise my gun to my eye
Never stop to wonder why
Then I saw the pink moon
My loving hit the ceiling with a splash of red
No need to ever have an HIV test
Now that it is no longer a death sentence
Always better to live dangerously where you can

Study me, Hanif, with your essays of poetry
Try to find the reason
That I pulled the trigger of the gun
Think of me
Do not think of James
There is more to his young athletic body
Than meets the observer's eye
Remember me to him in your essays
I know I will miss
The nights talking and flirting on that steep staircase

RICHARD'S LAST RAMBLE

I am thinking about giving up this rambling life
Living out of a broken suitcase
Living out of a broken body
Feel like I have had enough of these lonesome highway blues
I am thinking about giving up this rambling life
Because it has been carrying me away from you

I am thinking about giving up this travelling life
Jumping trains, jumping planes, taking photos
Sleeping in hotel vacuums, catching my death
Feel like I have spent too much time with the short-circuit
  demons in my head
I am thinking about giving up this travelling life
Because it has made me drift far away from you

I am thinking about giving up chasing all those other girls
They won't age as well as you
Under the microscope they don't match up to you now
Just fleeting excitements, to stroke the worst hubris inside my
  bloodstream
I am going to give up chasing all those other girls
I hate my reflection in the mirror
I need to find a way across the oceans to get to you

Flight bans, travel bans, high-risk countries and never-ending
  lockdowns
Nothing is going to stop me
Swimming across the oceans and getting to you

CHARLEMAGNE

King of the Franks
King of the Lombards
Emperor of the Romans
Son of Pepin the Short
I wanted to be like you
Oh, I wish I had as many concubines as Charlemagne
With numerous illegitimate children
And uniting the whole of Western and Central Europe
Oh, I wish I had built an empire like yours

None of these things matter, you tattered Nashville dog
Get off your self-obsessed highway
And just make a big sustained difference to one person
So Christmas day every day will be great every year
Come back
Come back
Bruce Springsteen
To me now
And let my armies be
The gentle mornings, the scared evenings
And the birds flying low through the summer sky
Into the garden I built for you

GUIDED BY VOICES

I loved you no more
After the Hundred Years' War
Canonised a Roman Catholic saint
My heroine or saviour you ain't

Your father collected taxes
You stretched me to the maxes
Not nineteen forever
Illiterate, yet Jean de Metz knew, clever

'I must be at the King's side'
Not spinning wool as a would-be peasant bride
Soldier-like, dressed as a man
You broke through the countryside – do what you can

Turn the conflict into a religious war
Galvanised through visions, guided by voices
Make us all realise what life we are fighting for

The Dauphin checked your goals
The Holy Spirit found no holes
You commanded the military through the night
Showed the war-weary redemption and a new light

Yet to the English you were possessed by the Devil
Captured and tried for heresy
'May God put me in his Grace'
Take you out of this world to a safer place
Frantically told cross-dressing was a sin
Evading rape, evading torture and from the prison you were
  in
Burnt at the stake, 30th May 1431, ashes thrown into the Seine
All of us damned now, no spiritual mystics, no martyrs again

But, Maid of Orleans, I love you no more
I have denounced God
And given up life to my core

BOB GUCCIONE JUNIOR

I just don't want to end up like Bob Guccione Junior
As I walk out of the Wholefoods on Eighth and Grand
That would be the nadir
Come to the City of Angels to create
Not to make money or imitate
I hope the new stardrops don't antagonise me

Just like you I have my vices, Bob
But I stepped out of my family's shadow
Built a world out of controlled rebellion
Took the Albion Ship over the Atlantic Ocean
And I would never dream of writing rhyming poetry
Well, just once about Joan of Arc
But she was an exception to the rule
I hope the new bums on Figueroa don't antagonise me

Back in my bungalow off Melrose
Pretty tied up, hanging upside down
My world is closing in
I need to abort the mission, start from scratch
Fall in love with the basics again
Fall in love with the mission
Fall in love again with the canvass process
Stay away from the Abbey and West Hollywood
Otherwise I am going to end up like Bob Guccione Junior
Just because you are winning it doesn't mean you are the
    lucky one

DEATHLETTER

To my son
Although I created you
You will never truly get to know your father
I was a troubadour of my time
Wrote to you of Lorca
Wrote to you of sado-masochism
Wrote to you of the lonesome hobo being beaten up
And you are pretty good-looking (for a boy)

To my doomed and damned son
Follow me, but don't follow me
You will have an even better voice than mine
Use it to find your dream brother
Use it write your death letter
And sing of a Yard of Blonde Girls
But you will never escape my shadow
Although you are better-looking than me (as a boy)

To my drowning son
Drowning in the Mississippi River to Led Zeppelin
You will always try too hard to emulate your father
You are not Bob Dylan
You will never be the logical poet
But a hundred inevitables will praise you
So burn bright, sing your heart out at Sine
And I will meet you up here for a concert one day

BALBOA PARK REVISITED

Hurry, hurry, because the girl you love is dead
Pack up your suitcase
And get out to the team at Balboa Park
Then you can say goodbye properly

The Wipe-Out gang killed her
They had flown in from Harlem and from England
I didn't know I loved her until
I saw her dead and cold there on the ground

I walked away and sought out the insanity factory
Weary to avoid phoney philosophers
And I got up this morning, at break of day
And I hugged hard the pillows where my girl used to lie

LIKE GEORGE MCFLY

My baby has a heart of stone
Nothing I can do to get her on her own
I try to tell her about all my feelings
But she just tells me she has to go to summer school
Like Heathcliff I beat my head on a tree until it bleeds
And I go back and try to impress her in front of all her friends
'Hey, I saw you at a corner store last week…'
Uh huh, George McFly, this conversation isn't going anywhere
Her long blonde hair giggles at me
She can see empty hotel rooms
That I will always sleep in
She smiles and turns back to her friends
As blood trickles down my adolescent slacker forehead
The two piercings on her face
Are arguing with each other about the colour of the southern
  California rain
I let all my emotions out in a loud voice
Let's build a family together, let's build a home
But she chooses summer school instead
And one more facial piercing (to remind me of my pain)
A boy's best friend is in his own head
'Sister, do you even know my name?'

THE AGE OF INNOCENCE

Did we finally make it past the age of innocence?
Did we make it through the Mayan apocalypse?
Did we find our way home on the 303?
Don't ask me I gotta move
Don't ask me I gotta move
You chased me away
By ignoring my calls
By ignoring my messages
By mocking my bad luck
I always stuck up for you

We both made it past the age of innocence
But not together, as broken people worlds apart
You in Australia, never gonna have a baby now
Serious problems are coming our way
Naomi, Naomi, Naomi
You are soul-dead in the AC/DC Lane gloom
And I won't ever see you again now
Don't ask me I gotta move
Don't ask me I gotta move

THE FISHERMAN

The Fisherman rows his boat in my direction
On the calm lilac sea of my youth
I can see him very well around the gloaming
And I wade through the water bearing gifts

But he isn't there for long (in my mind)
And disappears in daylight and darkness
And the rest of my day is a box-ticking exercise
As I drift through days in the lockdown ennui

There is a madman out there on the waves
And his boat on the reef could rescue me
If the Fisherman wanted to rescue the Fool
But he doesn't
He just wants to catch fish
And tempt me onto the beach
So I become like the Arawak men and women
With no premonitions of the hell to come

WELCOME TO THE NINETIES

I remember in the summer of 1990
Buying the Stranglers Greatest Hits
Because I loved 'Golden Brown' from an old compilation love
  cassette
I bought at an Our Price after school in the west

Welcome to the greatest decade of your life
After the fall of the Berlin Wall
Before the horrors of the War on Terror
There was a simplicity and a spontaneity
To life before the rise of the internet and social media
Those great Glastonbury, Phoenix and Reading festivals
The grunge bands and the Britpop explosion
The renaissance of Neil Young, Bob Dylan and Van the Man
Lose your virginity
Make your best friends for life
Watch Trainspotting *and* The Shawshank Redemption *over*
  and over again
See Paul Gascoigne's goal now and the dentist's chair
TFI Friday, Loaded *magazine and New Labour*
The zeitgeist felt right

210

But it was the Stranglers Greatest Hits *that kick-started it all*
  that summer
'Strange Little Girl'
'No More Heroes'
'Golden Brown'
About a girl's hair colour, right?
And what the hell was a Clit-Ar-Is anyway?
Dave Greenfield, what a legend you were
You started it all with those great keyboard moves
Taken from us today by the Great Pandemic
The pentagram represents the microcosm
As opposed to the macrocosm
The relation between the self and the universe

MANCHESTER BLUES

Takeaway coffee in my right hand
Left hand on the steering wheel
Bound for the wild blue yonder
Won't be back in the dirty old town for a long time now
Goodbye Manchester

I saw the ghost of Ian Curtis cross the Epping Walk Bridge
On Princess Road as I drove out of there for the last time
He told me I stayed there one year too long
Go discover Nashville and Austin, Texas
Go speak to the ghost of Townes Van Zandt

Manchester girls are wild tattooed angels
They told me to get away and go find myself again
I will come back and see them one day in double denim
When my skin is leathery with moonshine and California sun
I hit the M62 and turn up the music

Pink moon on my dashboard
Rock-and-roll death songs screeching down the motorway
Salford indie boys, I won't befriend you no more
The People's History Museum you have my Marxist heart
  always
Goodbye Manchester
Until we meet again

LIVING IN A CITY OF SEX ADDICTS

Living in a city of sex addicts
Is bound to have an impact on you
Sunshine skies go on forever
I don't need to go travelling
The best orgasms are all to be found here

Down the Abbey he was a she
In the Mother Lode and Flaming Saddles
She was a he and they all sparkle and shine
Like Coco Louise
I don't need to go travelling
The best orgasms are all to be found here

Another blue and another blue and another blue
Gotta stay away from the Ventura Boulevard vampires
Draining my money on the legal highs
It matters what car you drive in this city
And I drive from place to place
And I am close to no one
And no one notices me here
Baby, please come back home to me
I peaked a few years ago
And the orgasms count for nothing now
Might even end up like Mike Hutchence
Obsessing on auto-erotic asphyxiation
I don't need to go travelling
When living in a city of sex addicts

BLACKSTAR

David Bowie knew 2016 was gonna be bad
So he died at the start of the year
Just after releasing that Blackstar *album*
Rehearsed and rehearsed walking the streets of New York City
North wind is blowing down Third Avenue
Past the Gramercy Kitchen
Make mine a triple shot of cyanide
Death hangs in the Manhattan air
As drinking holes celebrate the lonely and tortured artists
You can't make great art without pain
I gotta fuck myself up
To improve my poetry
Get a dominatrix to do it for me in Hell's Kitchen
Red sunset is the colour of the end of time
As the sky bleeds onto the Hudson River
Predicting bad news and great art
So that we keep on rotting on the edge of the city that never
*   wakes up*
So that the beast in us is never fully unleashed on the Brooklyn
*   nineteen-year-old*
Play Blackstar *to myself*
Play The Next Day
Play Aladdin Sane
Play The Man Who Sold the World
To stay alive and see the new decade in

SAD GABRIELLA

When the hustlers have stolen your purity and innocence
And the wounded gypsy in you rises to the surface
When you are done with the frat boys and the magazine
* memory*
And the fire dancing has lost its appeal
That is when I will declare my love for you

When all the teardrops have washed away your reckless youth
And the days aren't long enough for all your painting
When showing up late means you got your contact lenses in
And you can see a brighter present, sad Gabriella
That is when I will declare my love for you

POEM FOR FREDDIE MERCURY

You were my imaginary friend as a teenager
Farokh Bulsara
And we hung out in our parents' gardens
Standing up on the stone walls and imitating Hendrix
And singing 'My Fairy King'

I would have been a better friend than Paul Prenter
Stayed loyal and kept you focused
You would have come to my family Christmas
In '86, '87, '88, '89 and '90
But why are you not here in '91
My young boy asks me
To sing 'Thank God It's Christmas' in the cold midnight mass
   church

I would have been a good friend to you
Farokh Bulsara
I would have goofed around with you like Kenny Everett
On a seaside rendezvous or playing a millionaire waltz
Kept you grounded though 'Mr Fahrenheit'
Teased you for your teeth
Sat over your deathbed with commitment and pride
Like a famous red-tailed hawk in disguise

JOEY RAMONE

Oh, to be a liberal in a world of conformity
Oh, to be Joey Ramone
Lanky kid from Queens
With obsessive compulsive disorder
Running up and down stairs
Touching my right side
As much as my left side
Oh, to look as cool as Joey Ramone
Ripped jeans, leather jacket and a cartoon band
New album out every fucking year
And to influence every punk-rock kid that ever lived
There are Ramones guitars
Seeping through my ceiling
Hitting the top of my brain
To tell me to keep it short and sweet to stay alive again
Oh, to be Joey Ramone
And only ever fall in love once
And have her stolen off you by the snake who is your business
    partner
It ain't my place in the nine-to-five world
And the Ku Klux Klan took my baby away
And to live with that life forever
And to live with that death forever

NEW DAWN FADES

I once was an idealist
I once saw the good in everyone
Every Saturday night could be a party
Every drink had the potential to show the divine
Yet innocence gets lost
And a new dawn emerges
There are a few things I no longer believe
A businessman who wants to change the world
A woman with a timely accusation
A snake when it is motionless
And the sea when it looks calm and innocent
Here is to the new dawn
Here is to the world after the coronavirus
And no one cares about my sinful past
When we all connect better
And the new dawn fades

THIS BEARD IS FOR REBECCA

Well, we all need someone to hug sometimes
I really miss those hugs right now
Social distancing kills intimacy
For someone who is a midnight gambler
To make up for it
All I can do is grow a beard
This beard is for Rebecca
And the next time I see her

Her spirit is pure and positive
In her smile she carries the diamonds from the mine
She sticks up for her man
When all the world doubts him
She sits on the banks of all the rivers in Essex
Waiting patiently, she brings steadfast belief and consistency
To me when I am all over the place
And on Mondays she squeezes her lemon
Stops me and him from becoming too satanic
And the street preachers from becoming too condescendingly
  messianic
In the absence of hairdressers
I keep growing this greying shaggy beard
This beard is for Rebecca
And the next time I see her

WHAT TO DO? KATHMANDU

It is all getting too much for me as a teenager
My vision fell on the seventeen tall candles at my table
The alcohol, the crushing hangovers
The knowledge I am not like everybody else
The mainstreamers and the popular
What to do? Kathmandu

It is all getting too much for me in my twenties
The sound of the inquisitorial voices merging
The drugs, the crazy relationships
The peer pressure to conform
The parasites and the vultures
What to do? Kathmandu

It is all getting too much for me in my thirties
The blackness of darkness supervened
The ticking body clock, the manipulators
The people earning more money than they should
The thieves and the bloodsuckers
What to do? Kathmandu

It is all getting too much for me in my forties
Arousing from the most profound of slumbers
The quest for immortality and immortal poetry

221

Will I ever have children to look after me in my old age?
The freeloaders and the snakes in the grass
What to do? Kathmandu

I make the decision now
Whilst I am tottering on the brink
Before I faint and fall into the abyss
To go and live again in Kathmandu and find a happy life!

NEEDLE OF DEATH

I guess you have to experience it before you knock it
Woe is love, my dear
And the great poets were hooked on the stuff
Dancing with 'Mister Brownstone'
Don't bring Harry
To see the needle and the damage done
Happiness is a warm gun
Get a grip on yourself though
Don't end up like Flava Flav
Experience it and move on
Don't get hooked like Love and Cobain
There she goes again
Racing perfectly through my brain
The needle is my friend
The needle is my sister
The needle is my philosopher
I am a fanatic for her
The needle of death

GIRL IN THE MOONLIGHT

Sun-tanned hippy girl in the moonlight
Will you be my lover?
I climbed up into your bedroom uninvited from the street below
I could be your killer or your rapist
But I know you trust my powerful femininity
I climbed through your window
In the sweating betwixt and between
I have a problem with doors
And I have a problem with questions and answers
Sun-tanned hippy girl in the moonlight
Will you be my lover?
I can tell you are lost
I only see this because I am lost too
Your father will not approve
But we need to run away and hit the open highway
*And play doo-wop music and sing to each other in foreign
   languages*
Until the desert gas stations become sign posts to Heaven
And our children are born in communes of immigrant splendour

REFUGEES WELCOME HERE

Syrian refugees scattered on dusk's highway wailing
The racists do not understand their pain
Yet I, as a child, had discovered
That I could have spoken up
Had it not been for a handkerchief
Tied heavily into my mouth
By my over-protective parents
Who were mentally repeating some passages
Of the 'Omnipresence of the Deity'

Refugees are welcome here

Malala Yousafzai spoke up
When she was surrounded by hate
Youngest Nobel Prize laureate
Agrees with me
As she guarantees the education of women
Battles the Taliban
And shows that one voice makes a difference

NEEDLE IN MY VEIN

Needle in my vein
Needle in my vein
You are helping me to forget the nightmares of my childhood
And I am getting skinnier every day
Strung out and elegantly wasted
Needle in my vein

Like Pete Doherty and Kate Moss in 2005
Me and you gonna learn to forget
Skip out of the studio
To a jazz band's drumming beat
Needle in the vein

This could be the death of both of us
But I gotta keep remembering to learn to forget
Lie back on the floor to Lust for Life
This life can't be beat
Needle in the vein

People who are out there trying to help you
Just don't understand the pain you are going through
And the thrill of stealing and robbing
The chase ain't necessarily better than the catch
Needle in the vein

My bandmates might throw me out
But my girl is hooked on this life too
She understands the mystique of Richey Manic
So we symbiotically keep going
To fake our own fake reported disappearances
Needle in the vein